how to be a

Yoga Rockstar

MARTIN D. CLARK

Published by:

OMG Books

WWW.OMGBOOKS.CO.UK

be present

how to be a
Yoga Rockstar

ISBN: 978-0993184406 **DESIGN:** GRAHAM WILLIAMS / **PRINTING:** SYMBIAN PRINT / **COPYRIGHT:** MARTIN D. CLARK

define yourself

Inside:

---

life is awesome

What is a yoga rockstar?

WHO KNEW YOGA WOULD PRODUCE THE NEXT GENERATION OF ROCK STARS? IF YOU DID, THEN YOU'RE A GENIUS AND I WANT YOU TO TELL ME NEXT WEEK'S WINNING LOTTERY NUMBERS

Yoga is the new rock and roll. Well, sort of. Yes, there are a few glaring differences: yoga teachers are more likely to be caught philosophising over green smoothies post-workout, while rock stars are often too inebriated to talk at all, whether that's under the influence of drugs, alcohol, or plain stupidity.

But there are also similarities. We love our rock stars. They bring technicolour to our lives; they entertain us, and bring us joy.

Yoga teachers are no different. For their students, they have the ability to inspire, to entertain, to educate and to heal, much like the therapeutic powers of music itself. Alas, one glaring difference is the pay gap between the two. When rock stars shift their MP3s by the millions, they get paid handsomely for their work.

Yoga teachers, on the other hand, may be changing people's lives just as profoundly (perhaps more so), but getting recognised for that contribution to the greater good isn't always easy.

This book is an attempt to redress the balance.

So, put on your shades future yoga rock star, and head out into the bright lights. Your stage beckons you.

So what is a yoga rock star?

I conducted some very unscientific research into the above question (basically I asked around a bit). Here's what some people said:

"It's just another LA term reflecting the popularity of yoga these days "

"A yoga teacher so famous that even people who don't do yoga would've heard of them"

Shout it from the rooftops

THE FACT THAT YOU HAVE PICKED UP THIS BOOK
SUGGESTS THAT YOU HAVE ALREADY BEEN 'FOUND' BY
YOGA. DON'T BE SHY ABOUT IT, OR THE SECRETS THAT
YOU NOW KNOW. GO TELL THE WORLD.

There's an old saying: you don't find yoga, it finds you. What the heck does that mean? It means that at some point you have stumbled into a class, picked up a book, or maybe had a chance encounter with a stranger: something that has, perhaps inadvertently, exposed you to the world of yoga, in all its many guises.

Surely that means it was 'me' that found it then, not the other way round?

In a sense, yes. Maybe you were experiencing a tough time in your life in which you sought some guidance or release. Maybe you needed to lose weight or shake off stress so your GP pointed you in the direction of that first class.

So, yes, that's possibly true. But once you have discovered yoga - or it has found you (whatever!) - it's the start of a life-long affair. It doesn't always happen overnight (although many do float out of their first class totally smitten); it may take time, possibly years, for yoga to weave its crafty magic upon you.

And it can be a strange process as these seemingly innocuous exercises on a rubber mat (ethically sourced, of course) starts to shift things within you and all around you.

Not just in re-aligning your bones, but in shaping a whole new outlook to life and all things around you. Yoga is potent stuff. You better believe it.

ACCESS ALL AREAS

This growing mind-body awareness permeates all areas: from your relationship with yourself (your self-confidence grows, your posture straightens, your smile broadens) and with others, to your new health conscious creations in the kitchen.

While the rest of the family's chowing down on burgers, you're chopping up celery sticks and experimenting with kelp and algae; ah, the fun never ends!

Indeed, yoga's ability to transform, to heal, to inspire, to console, is nothing short of remarkable. It is a true gift from the ancients that we are lucky to benefit from today. Who then, once bitten by this wonder bug, would not want to spread the word, to pass on this magic to others? That is why so many choose to become yoga instructors; to inspire others to realise their own greatness.

Yoga is awesome. You are awesome. Becoming a yoga teacher is not a career move; it's your chance to change the planet, one beautiful person at a time. Now get to it. Don't shirk your destiny.

1

Your Journey
Starts Here

take your time

"*I won't be a rockstar,
I will be a legend*"

Freddie Mercury

"Do what you love and you will never work another day in your life"

Spread the love...

...(BUT DON'T GIVE UP THE DAY JOB YET)

YOGA IS A BIG PART OF YOUR **LIFE.** MAYBE YOU EVEN LOVE YOGA. AND THAT IS A VERY **BEAUTIFUL** THING. SO WHY NOT SPREAD THE **LOVE** AND TEACH YOGA

Imagine the impact you could have: changing lives, inspiring others, healing hurts; all the giggles and the fun to be had. Ah, the bliss...

The trouble is you still have to go to work: at the bank, at the grocery store, maybe even running the country (well, you never know who's reading!).

And all of that gets in the way of your wondrous yoga practice. What a bummer.

If you were the boss you could be stretching your 'thang' on the mat all day long, every single day. Heaven.

So, it's simple - just ditch your job. Whoa, hold on a minute. Alas, life's not quite like that; people keep asking you for money (water, gas, even iPhones do not come free. Plus there are a zillion other things to be paid for).

How then, you ask, can I go on and live my dream to bring yoga to the world, to make people shine when I have to pay the rent?

And that's a very good question.

Unfortunately, it's not an easy one to answer. Making a living teaching yoga is challenging to say the least. It can be hard work, often with little financial reward, especially in those early days.

Now that doesn't sound much like rock and roll, does it?

But it can be done. How do I know? Because many others have done it before you; and many are doing it today right now.

And this book will show you how you can do it.

So buckle up and let's begin.

just remember this future yoga rock star...

...that when you do take to the stage: the world wants and needs your divine gift; your inspirational, most amazing, yoga teaching..

and it is more than willing to pay for it too.

Now isn't that a good bit of news?

Why oh why?

SO YOU GO **HOME** ONE DAY AND TELL YOUR PARTNER THE **GOOD NEWS:** "HI HONEY, I'M GOING TO BE A **YOGA TEACHER!**"

And guess what happens next...he (or she) retorts either kindly: "OMG, you'll make the best goddamn yoga teacher this world's ever seen!"; or less kindly: "Are you out of your mind? Don't you think we've had enough of all that crazy hippie stuff already?"

Or, most probably, with great (and fairly accurate) pragmatism: "Cool, you'll be a great teacher. But who's gonna pick up the kids from school? And will we still be able to make end's meet if you ditch the day job?"

Okay, so everyone's different and facing their own unique set of circumstances. Not all of us have day jobs to relinquish; not all of us have kids. Some are more solvent than others. For every single mum out there on the breadline, there's a bored housewife with an investment banker husband there to take the sting out of any career transition and pick up the monthly mortgage payment. Most of us probably fall somewhere between the two.

Still, sooner or later, you'll most likely come across some of these practical and very real challenges, even objections.

No one said this was going to be easy.

And yet...whether you want to be a yoga teacher, a fitness instructor, or a lion tamer, the price of NOT following your dreams may be incalculable. More on this later.

laugh often

The world at your feet

HERE'S A **FUN, FUN, FUN** CAREER CHECKLIST

If you're on the fast-track to success. yoga rockstardom may not happen overnight but follow this blueprint for the big time and you'll be bankrolling your own Manhattan studio in no time at all.

To Do List...

1. Take up yoga   2. Get qualified ASAP   3. open your own studio

4. Lead luxury retreat to Costa Rica, Bali etc...

5. Be a Magazine cover star

6. Teach yoga to the president (or Madonna, Gwyneth Paltrow, etc.)

7. Make a million bucks   8. Bring about world peace

9. win Nobel Peace Prize (for bringing about world peace)

10. Retire on private island (hang out with sir Richard Branson, and other rich & famous folk.)

Don't do it

THERE ARE PLENTY OF **GOOD** REASONS NOT TO BECOME A YOGA TEACHER. THE **TRUTH** IS IF YOU KEEP YOUR JOB AT THE BANK, OR THE INSURANCE OFFICE, OR AS A HOMEMAKER, AND OPT NOT TO BECOME A YOGA **SUPERSTAR...**

YOU'LL MOST LIKELY ENJOY A FAR MORE RELIABLE AND PREDICTABLE INCOME (AND PROBABLY OTHER PERKS TOO)

YOUR WORK LIFE WILL BE UNAFFECTED, MEANING YOU RETAIN THE SAME STRUCTURE TO YOUR WEEK

THAT MEANS YOU CAN COLLECT THE KIDS ON TIME AND COOK THEIR DINNERS AS BEFORE

PLUS YOU'LL SAVE YOURSELF ALL THE TROUBLE OF ENDLESS HOURS OF YOGA STUDY. PHEW!

AND IT'LL COST YOU NOTHING IN EXPENSIVE TUITION FEES IF YOU CHOOSE NOT TO GO AHEAD

Yep, there are plenty of very good reasons not to become a yoga teacher. However, life cannot always be measured in logic or dollar bills. It's important to follow your passion if you are to live a truly rich and satisfing life.

fear is not real

Great expectations

BEING **CLEAR** ABOUT WHAT YOU'RE TAKING ON IS AWAYS A **GOOD** PLACE TO **START**

All it means is you need to be crystal clear why you're doing this. Teaching yoga can be a life changing event in all sorts of ways. But it doesn't have to be. Many people want to train as a teacher simply to deepen their own practice for the love of yoga.

In fact, it's estimated that up to half of all people undertaking teacher training have no intention of going on to actually teach. They just love yoga that much. How cool is that!

If you've been bitten by the yoga bug but you love your job protecting gorillas or hauling long distance freight trucks across the country then this option makes perfect sense. Keep your job and still study yoga; it's the best of both worlds.

CAREER MOVE

But what if you are looking to do this as a full-time career? That's an entirely different ball game. And that, my friend, is what brings us together here. This will be our focus from now.

Again, there are different expectations on this as well. While some might be content to run one or two classes a month for a bit of extra pocket money, or even just to maintain a work or social life in their later years, others are on the fast-track to success.

We're talking ambitious 21-year-olds hungry for fame and fortune. Then there are former dancers, even TV stars, looking to take their skills out to a new audience. It takes all sorts.

This book will assist you whatever your background, whichever way you decide to go. If you're just looking to earn a little extra cash, or drum up a few new students, that's fine. Pore over the marketing tips and social media skills to lift your yoga business up no matter how modest or humble your expectations.

But if it is yoga rock star status that you seek, then, of course, you're in the right place.

BEAUTIFUL YOU

Take note, however: as in the rock & roll world, the competition for superstardom can be intense. There are lots of brilliant teachers out there.

Luckily, you have one amazing thing in your favour that makes it entirely possible, even probable, that you will succeed: YOU.

There is no one else like you. No one else is able to replicate what you do, whatever your ability level on the mat. No one else even comes close to being you. You are unique. And it is you that gets to write your own unique chapter in yoga history. Starting NOW.

YOGA ROCKSTAR TIP #1

'INSPIRE STUDENTS'

"Inspire your students to be themselves. Watching them blossom into wonderful yoga teachers is worth its weight in gold"

Jill Lawson | USA

great things await

Motivation

MOTIVATION = **ENTHUSIASM, DRIVE, AMBITION, INITIATIVE, DETERMINATION, ENTERPRISE,** GET UP AND GO (YOU GET THE PICTURE)

You'll need plenty of this stuff. Even if you're just looking to train up as a teacher, and never actually teach, you've got to be motivated to get through all that hard work (and there's plenty of that).

And if you are looking for yoga rock stardom then be prepared to muck in, get your hands dirty, and hang on in there when the going gets tough.

Those lucky yogis and yoginis that do reach the top of the tree need to be at the top of their game to make it there. There's typically no short cut to hard work whatever business you're in.

In the music biz, don't think The Beatles achieved immortality without putting in a bit of legwork too pulling all-nighters at dodgy Hamburg night clubs long before Love Me Do hit the charts. And then there's Charlie Watts, the laid back drummer of The Rolling Stones, who once said that he'd spent most of his career just hanging around in airports.

The same goes for yoga. Any of today's yoga superstars will tell you the same.

Motivation is what'll make the difference between success and failure. If you really want it - and the motivation is there from the off - then you'll get there. But if you're struggling with your get up and go, then you'll struggle to make an impact in whatever walk of life you're in. Whether that's teaching yoga asana or basic accountancy.

The best news is that motivation is free. It's abundant and easy to access.

Getting your unlimited supply of this wonderful stuff is simple provided you are passionate about what you are doing. If you truly are, then getting going, staying motivated, and sticking to your plans - whatever obstacles come up - will follow quite naturally.

Get inspired

BETHANY PLATANELLA WAITED A YEAR BEFORE LEADING HER FIRST CLASS

Bethany Platanella USA

I didn't plan to teach immediately | My only plan after training was to find any job to pay my rent. Yoga is not the most lucrative job, especially in the beginning, so it wasn't even on the table for me to start teaching.

I found a studio where I wanted to teach | Once I found the right studio, I went to class every single day. Sometimes I was the only one there, sometimes I wasn't. Through my strong, regular practice and intensive teacher training, I was unknowingly making an impression on the owner. One day she asked me flat out: "I need a sub, will you cover for me?" I told her I wasn't ready. She kept at me for months until I finally gave in.

The scariest part is just stepping up | I taught my first class to a group of three. It was scary. I thought they hated it. I couldn't remember my left side from my right; I couldn't remember anything, When I finished, it felt like gallons of water filled with anxiety and nerves poured out of me. My students clapped and praised me. It felt amazing. I was hooked. After two or three classes you will probably have tackled the fear and feel excited to make your teaching your own.

I am absolutely confident in my teaching | I know I'm a good teacher, not because my students tell me, and it isn't because my ego's talking. It's because I tell myself that it's true. When I walk into a room full of students, I feel confident. Manifestation is important in most aspects of life, but exceptionally so when you are acting as a leader. You have to feel confident and believe in yourself. By repeating 'I am a good yoga teacher' - to yourself and also to others - it will become your truth.

There are financial challenges | It's difficult to throw yourself fully into yoga when the cost of daily life insists you have a more lucrative side job. I'd love to immerse myself in workshops and retreats, and to teach full time. Financially, it's a challenge.

lead by example

best advice:

Go to as many classes as you can.
Give every class your all.
Make your presence known.

Robert Sturman (USA)

PHOTOGRAPHER

WHAT'S THE SECRET TO CAPTURING AMAZING YOGA ASANA ON CAMERA?

My images start from the ground up | I'm usually very low when shooting. This is important to me because we have a better chance at isolating the figure, so there's more clarity when we see it. So often the pose gets lost, but if we are looking up at it, and maybe there is a plain background like the sky, then the asana is going to look like a gorgeous and proud sculpture.

This is especially true for arm balances | It'll read more clearly if you see the background underneath the subject. If I was higher up, looking down, it would not register that something incredible was occurring - that the yogi is lifting off. Even if it's a small sliver of sky underneath it will make a huge difference in presenting the pose as colossal.

Look for the stillness between the breath | It is between the inhale and the exhale that the stillness exists most prominently. That is when I choose to press the shutter. The more still I am, the more clear I am. I aspire to only press the button one time. It is a zen.

Press the button and move on | I do not subscribe to the guessing game in photography - the idea that if I ferociously make enough exposures, I just might get something nice. It has always felt cleaner for me to breathe, see, and record the decisive moment. There's nothing wrong with pressing the button one time and moving on.

Camera phones are great too | I'm not attached to any particular app, so I explore new ones all the time. A few I've used are Photoshop, Mill Colour, Perfect Photo, Pro HDR, and Instagram (the filters are awesome). But always start with a great image that you love, never depend on the app. Then, when you take it on a postproduction journey, you're just infusing a little more of your soul into it. Have fun.
Really connect with your subject | I used to 'take'

photographs, until one day I realised that taking is stealing. Now I connect with my subject and, through our shared humanity, we make a photograph. It's more about loving what you are seeing and being inspired by how beautiful yoga is.

"It is between the inhale and the exhale that the stillness exists most prominently. That is when I choose to press the shutter"

YOGA ROCKSTAR TIP #2

'SUCCESS WILL FIND YOU'

"While business and yoga can be hard to meld because of what may look like conflicting principles, keep a good, but logical heart and mind, and success will find you. It is possible. Anything is."

Debbie Lynn | *USA*

create magic

How much can I earn?

WHILST EARNING A LIVING FROM **YOGA** IS **INFINITELY** POSSIBLE, **STRIKING** IT 'RICH' IS A FAR MORE ILLUSIVE THING

Sorry if this question sounds crass, but it's pretty fundamental. Perhaps you've been seduced by the glamour life your own instructor apparently leads; maybe they've been booked to spend the summer teaching A-list celebs in Tuscany in Italy. Yes, it happens (I know that yoga teacher. And I know that A-list celeb. The lucky swines!).

Sadly, the vast majority will struggle to reach these lofty heights. Let's just say don't follow a yoga career at all if that's what you're after.

In reality, you can expect your reward for following your yoga dream to be anything from pennies to mega bucks (though not musical rock star megabucks, sadly, unless you get a part-time gig touring with The Rolling Stones).

You'll most likely start small, picking up the odd few classes or lessons here and there. So how much you earn will be directly linked to how many classes you take. Only your expectations and lifestyle can determine how much is 'enough' in this sense.

At this stage you'll be paid to teach and not much more than that, although that's not a bad thing as you learn the ropes. The more classes you take, the more you'll earn; it's a great way to boost your income, but it also means you're taking on more work.

It's only later, as your experience and reputation both grow, that you can start to boost your earnings in other ways (workshops, retreats, festival appearances).

That's when the bigger rewards (financial, and other) start to kick in.

If you do hit the big time, then you will not be worrying about money. Bikram Choudhury is said to own a fleet of Rolls-Royce cars, for instance.

But that's for the future. For now, manage your expectations. The potential is there but that really shouldn't be your primary motivation. If you're in this for the money, get out now, and go look for a big investment bank that's hiring.

Above all, don't shoot me in the street for mentioning money in a book about yoga. It's something that affects us all, whether we like it or not.

As one bright spark (Edith Wharton) once said: "The only way not to think about money is to have a great deal of it." Until that day, I'm afraid that we - yes, that includes you - are going to have to think about it.

Where do yoga teachers come from?

YOGA TEACHERS COME FROM ALL WALKS OF LIFE

It takes all sorts. Just as yoga itself draws in folks from pretty much every walk of life, so too does professional teaching. Anyone can do yoga. Anyone can be a yoga teacher.

There are, however, one or two walks of life that seem to attract a disproportionate share of new instructors. People coming from a dance background, for example. It's kind of a natural follow on, I guess.

There are plenty of ex-ballerinas now plying their trade in the yoga world. They are perfect candidates, at least in terms of their physical prowess and pliability. Of course, there are many other skills required - communication, empathy, and countless others - which are not the exclusive domain of the dancing queen.

Equally, there are those that groan at the very thought of yet another dancer or ballerina entering the world of yoga. They argue that this extreme flexibility - enviable, perhaps, but beyond the reach of many - can be detrimental to mere mortals, those students with no hope of mirroring their tutor's capabilities.

Extreme bendability is therefore not the only requirement here.

Whatever your line of work, or previous history, you'll fit in just fine.

Middle-aged men often come to yoga to deal with stress. Likewise, senior citizens may start to explore yoga as a means to keep active or stay socially connected. No one is better qualified than inspirational peers to spread the message among these groups.

It really does take all sorts. And that's what this yoga world needs. Find that unique voice of yours and no one will even notice if you can touch your toes.

BUT I'M TOO...TO BA A YOGA TEACHER

Stop that right now! There are plenty of 'old' yoga teachers out there doing it already, and there are 'fat' men and women teaching the world over. What would you say to your students if they asked you this?

'But I'm too male'

Don't be daft, the original yogis were all male too. Go to India. Check in at an ashram. See for yourself that men teach yoga too. Get enlightened, you crazy fool. A lot of male yoga teachers in the West are former martial arts experts. Try telling them they shouldn't be doing it. Actually, don't - you'll end up with a broken nose!

make the time

'But I'm too old'

There are people in their nineties still teaching yoga. Do you want to live your dream, or do you want to call it a day? You want to inspire others? There is no better example out there than seeing an 'old timer' take their place, centre stage, at the front of a class, and lead by example. You know what they say: 50 is the new 40. So let's crank it up a bit and make 90 the new 65! Lead the way or get out of the way.

Don't be preposterous: yoga is for everyone, no matter what your age, sex or (in)ability. It's so true. Yoga really is for every body. And that also means no one is excluded from teaching it either.

Look around you. Go searching for some comparable role models. If you're worried that you're 'past it' then take inspiration from those amazing teachers still working, still leading from the front in their nineties. Yes, it's true, they're out there. Some don't even start training until their eighties (yes, their eighties!). I know they're out there because I've met them.

Or check out stories of ordinary people that have had their lives turned around by yoga, only to then go on to teach it. The list includes prison inmates, sedentary office workers, TV presenters, cancer survivors. They all love their yoga and want to share it with others. **Don't let the scales or the amount of candles on your cake hold back your dreams.**

It's not about being fat or thin, young or old, male or female, it's about having the right intention, the right mindset. If yoga has truly 'found' you then you're qualified to start thinking about qualification as a yoga teacher to bring your light to the world.

If you've still got any lingering reservations about your size or age or whatever, here's one final piece of advice: Get over it. I'm not into any of that corporate stuff but in the famed words of famous sports shoe maker, Nike: **Just Do It.**

'But I'm too fat to teach yoga'

Are you serious? You do yoga and you're still fretting about your weight. Love yoga, love your body. There is no 'right' shape for doing yoga. We are who we are. Our society is preoccupied with Fat v Thin. Don't succumb to that shallow debate. The whole point of yoga is to transcend that garbage. And don't deprive others of your wisdom either. You are the ideal candidate to show that it can be done. Fat, thin, who cares? We are all beautiful on the inside. Life is a mere blink of the eye. If you've got it - and especially if you've got more of it - then flaunt it.

More yoga please

IT DOESN'T MATTER HOW YOU CAME TO **YOGA**. ALL ROUTES ARE **PERFECTLY FINE**

Before you make any big decisions it's important to experience a wide range of styles, teachers and classes to know precisely what you're after. It may help clarify what sort of career path you wish to follow.

Call it teacher training research if you like. Or just do it for the sheer love of yoga.

It will help you gain clarity and certainty when you finally commit to a teacher training programme. You may know that Kundalini Yoga is for you, for example, but surely it does no harm at all to check out what's going on next door, whether that's a traditional Iyengar class or the blistering heat of Bikram. Get out there and soak it all up. Enjoy yourself. Go crazy. Live it. Breathe it.

Remember: you're going to be a real, live - and sensational - yoga teacher. And the world can't wait to meet you.

Get to class NOW

USE YOUR **MAT** AS YOUR **ANCHOR** AS YOU GLIMPSE THAT **BIG,** BRIGHT NEW **FUTURE** AHEAD

Here's some more good news. When you finally arrive at the point where you know you want to be a yoga teacher the next step is remarkably simple: do more yoga. And lots of it too.

You've heard the old saying about us all being 'beginners', and its so true. (Though, to be fair, some of us are clearly more 'beginners' than others. Indeed, to misquote George Orwell's Animal Farm: "All yogis are equal, but some are more equal than others". Based on this, I'm practically plankton in the yoga food chain - no offence, plankton!).

Forget about all that. The fact is this is probably one of the most important lessons you'll learn from the mat. The sheer depth and amazing diversity of yoga means there really is always more to learn. With thousands of years of history behind it, you really could spend your entire life working out on the mat or poring over Sanskrit texts and only just scratch the surface.

Even if you do master a headstand what good is it if you have no connection with others, no appreciation for where your students are on their yoga journey, or how to make them realise their own greatness? Yoga is about more than being a show pony.

And if you are a show pony (and I know some yoga teachers that are) then you may well get a few gasps and wows from the crowd to feed your ego, but it doesn't make you the world's greatest teacher.

At this stage, your 'job' is to hone your skills on the mat, being mindful all the time of your true, longer-term intentions. By all means start investigating teacher training routes straight away, but never forget where your passion lies. Use your mat as your anchor, as you begin to dream and glimpse your beautiful new future ahead.

SECRET AGENT

Your secret mission at this stage - should you choose to accept it, 007 - is also to quietly observe your own teachers, to get a feel for how this might be different at the front of the class, looking into the eyes of the students, no matter what their level.

This is a terrific learning opportunity. Watch how your teacher interacts with their students before, during and after class. What's the atmosphere like in the room and to what extent is this created or driven by the teacher? Is it relaxed and informal, or quite regimented? Is there any banter or laughter going on? What about adjustments, the hands-on stuff?

Jot down afterwards what you like and didn't like about the session.

Different Strokes

VARIETY IS THE SPICE OF LIFE. AND SO IT GOES WITH YOGA AS WELL

The more yoga you do, the better you become at it. At least, that's normally how it works. Another consequence is that you get more of a feel for what you like and don't like. Some people live for hot yoga, others just pass out in the heat. You get the idea.

So, after all your hours on the mat, if you know which style is for you then just go for it.

But don't knock it until you've tried it. It's all very well dismissing hot yoga or this-that-and-the-other yoga as just a fad, but how do you know if you've not experienced it for yourself? What the hell, you might have a lot of fun doing it.

Snobbery over different styles or schools is one of the less attractive traits in yoga, and yet it's all too common. So don't ever be accused of it. Embrace this crazy world of yoga, with all its quirks and idiosyncrasies, and your open mind and heart will beam through to your students.

After all, there's room in the forest for all the animals.

You don't have to methodically try every single yoga class on the planet. But at least give a sprinkling of the better known ones a run for their money before you pick your path.

Different strokes

There are so many yoga styles out there, all uniquely presented by individuals bringing their own personalities into the room. So much to discover. But here's the best bit: even if you do favour one style over another it doesn't mean you're obligated forever. It's a bit like signing to play for a soccer team rather than supporting one. In yoga, you can do Bikram one day, and Kundalini the next. That's not true for us football supporters: as a life-long (and long-suffering) fan of English soccer team West Ham United (who haven't won a trophy in decades), my innate sense of loyalty means it's impossible to jump ship. Another big shout out for yoga!

shine your light

Get Inspired

SUSAN MYERS DITCHED A CORPORATE CAREER TO TRAIN AS AN ASHTANGA TEACHER

I've always been a risk taker
I thought I'd spend a year making a slow transition into teaching before leaving my job. In the end, I handed in my notice before I finished my training.

Teacher training is just the start
My course set me up to teach a class of relatively fit yoga teachers, not to have a career and not to deal with any eventuality. Research, more training and experience are giving me the tools for that. If you want to teach yoga then you need a strong, regular practice and to take the time to learn how to break everything down. After all, you never know who might turn up in your class.

It can be tough attracting students
It's really difficult to get enough students and get the word out there. I also thought there would be lots of demand for daytime classes, but there isn't as much I'd hoped. I think a web marketing course might have been a good idea during teacher training.

Not all teachers are angels | I was under the impression that all yoga teachers in the world were lovely people, but actually they are just people, some nice, some not so nice, some very suspicious and competitive. I still find it hard to understand why we don't all try to help each other; I guess I'm very naïve for an MBA graduate.

It has changed me personally | I tried to teach a few gentle yoga classes when I started out but that didn't work well because at that time I found it difficult to empathise with someone who needed a gentle approach. I think I'm getting a bit better at the empathy, but I still love the yang-style yoga.

It'll all come good | It can be frustrating, and hard on the ego (which I still have I'm afraid), but it'll all work out in the end. I have faith that if I continue to do what I love doing, I will find like-minded people who love what I love and become established.

best advice:

make sure you actually love yoga before you train; if you don't, don't bother. Your students will be able to tell your heart isn't in it. Oh and don't think it'll make you a millionaire: a career in yoga isn't a vow of poverty but it can be hard-going.

Susan Myers UK

Don't under-estimate what you are taking on. If you do intend to pursue a full-time yoga career, then get ready for some hard work too. Good things take time to build, and anything of value is rarely easy to achieve.

Do this for love - the love of yoga - and you can't go too far wrong. Start out with lofty financial goals, however, and you may be heading for big trouble.

ONE GIANT LEAP

Talk to as many teachers as possible to find out the day-to-day realities of the job.

Festivals and yoga shows can be a great way to experience lots of the world's top teachers all in one place and to meet other like-minded people.

Being a full-time teacher is very different to enjoying a couple of classes down the gym each week. That may be all you want at the end of the day.

Moving from that place to the position of a full-time yoga instructor is one giant leap.

It's all do-able. Just know what you're taking on.

be bold

But I want it NOW!!

COOL YOUR JETS **HOTSHOT.** IT TAKES TIME TO BUILD A **STRONG** CAREER

I once attended a yoga conference in the USA where young hopefuls were quizzing a few superstar teachers on how to 'make it'. I'll always remember one exuberant 20-year-old, so pumped and full of energy, that she almost had to be restrained. "How do I get on the circuit? How do I get to be a magazine cover girl? How do I get to work with celebrities?" In truth, she was an amazing sight, a real live-wire. If you could've bottled her zest and vitality you would have solved the world's energy crisis. Her classes must have been wild.

The panel, a mix of well-known and very established yoga teachers from a range of countries, were equally impressed. They too were blown away by her spirit and enthusiasm. There was also something very endearing about her youthful naivety too. The group of teachers, one by one, told her to slow down, to bide her time, and that the path will open up to her when she's good and ready.

One of the wise heads in the room reminded her (and all of us) of Shiva Rea's beautiful words: "Don't push the river".

If it's meant to be, it'll be. And I reckon there's no way of holding back that kind of raw energy for long. I don't know where she is now, but I'll bet with that dynamism of hers, if she can catch the river's current, and find the flow, then she'll do some pretty amazing work in the future. She probably is right now.

How I made it happen

TARA STILES EARNED WIDE SUCCESS AS AN ENTREPRENEUR, BUILDING STRALA INTO A GLOBAL EMPIRE WITH A PLAN ROOTED IN HELPING OTHERS

Look for the positives | Keep a positive attitude and a desire to help others, above anything else.

I've had quite a few lucky breaks | I've had a lot of magic moments; these have happened when hearts, intentions and efforts are in the right place. One was when a New York Times reporter showed up at my studio (Strala) to do a short post about me. She took a few classes and hung out with me for a while and felt connected and wanted to help spread the word. I asked her after a couple days why she was still hanging around. She told me she really loved what I was doing and pitched her editor to change the short. In the end, she made a five page cover story about me that brought a lot of early awareness when I first started building. A lucky moment, for sure.

You need a broad mix of skills | Gaining the tools to lead a class with grace and ease. Being comfortable and confident in communicating your passions. Being excited and willing to show up for opportunities that come your way, regardless of financials.

Social media can be a useful ally | Share what interests you. Don't buy followers. Keep it real online and you'll have a better understanding of who is actually interested in what you are sharing. Make it a conversation, not a game.

Personal motto | Follow how you feel.

Tara Stiles USA

follow your intuition

best advice:

*Positive attitude is everything.
People connect to how you make
them feel more than anything else.
Instructors that provide an open
space for people to feel into
themselves will make real
connections that help
people greatly.*

#2

Dream the (im)possible dream

just imagine

"*Energy is so important.
If you don't have it,
don't bother with
rock and roll*"

Yoko Ono

amaze yourself

Cat: where are you going?

Alice: which way should i go?

Cat: that depends on where you are going

Alice: i don't know

Cat: then it doesn't matter which
way to go

Lewis Carrol
Alice in wonderland

Just imagine

NOW'S THE TIME TO START VISIONING AND CREATING THE LIFE YOU ALWAYS DREAMED OF

O nce you know what you want in life, the rest is easy. If only that were true. I'm sure Neil Armstrong didn't wake up one morning, decide to go to the moon, only to find himself strapped into a rocket a few weeks later. I imagine it was the culmination of a lot of hard work and training.

Still, having a destination (it doesn't have to be the moon!) certainly helps a lot. If your destination is 'yoga teacher' then you have something tangible and exciting to work towards.

But how do you know if you want it enough? That's easy, because you'll start to feel passionate about it, you'll start to live that dream, and feel the energy stirring. Like yoga itself, your vision will permeate every little part of your being. This is really important.

That's because once you've got the passion - that fire inside you - your enthusiasm will help burn away the doubts and lift you into the stars.

If you're genuinely passionate about this, then you're probably cut out to be a yoga teacher.

Sounds obvious, but as many established teachers will tell you, you've got to feel that fire to be able to deliver to your students, to show up in class each and every time. It shows you're living the life you're meant to live.

If you've got that belief, the drive, the determination - whatever you call it - you're ready to start refining, shaping and crafting your new career.

You're ready to follow that passion.

Follow your dreams

YOGA MAKES YOU FEEL **ALIVE** SO IMAGINE THE **THRILL** OF TEACHING IT TO OTHERS

Action hero TV presenter Bear Grylls, a devout Christian and a father to three boys, has a great formula for living life to the full that he calls 'The Five F's'.

I've no idea if he does yoga or not (although he sure gets plenty of other exercise), and there's no way he's a vegetarian given all the bugs and insects he eats on his adventures, but he's a good all-round role model I'd say.

I believe 'The Five F's' offer a good template for us all.

The first four 'F's' are pretty obvious to most of us, I expect, but it's the fifth one that's really important here.

The Five F's...

Family – Friends – Faith – Fun

Follow Your Dreams

We only have one life. Don't waste yours doing work you feel nothing for.

Feel inspired by what you do.

Always follow your dreams. Even if the challenges in doing so may, at times, seem great, you'll feel alive every single day by pursuing it. No more dull, wasted days. Just a great life lived.

Yoga teaching can give you that life.

What's your destination?

Let's start working on that dream then shall we?

Let's assume the passion is there, and you're all set for a new career in yoga. Think about what that feels like for you.

Don't be put off by any practicalities at this stage. If you're more mature in years that doesn't stop you from becoming a highly sought after yoga teaching sensation. If you've got a real gift for it then you'll find that age is largely irrelevant. Even if you're in your nineties, what's to stop you becoming the nation's pre-eminent yoga guru for the seniors community? Lead by example. Be the change, that's what Gandhi told us.

And what if you're young, sexy and super stretchy? Then what's stopping you performing at the big yoga festivals, or gracing magazine covers? Nothing. Just you. Think as big as you like.

There are oceans of possibilities for all types out there. Indeed, not everyone wants to be taught by a superstar.

For instance, some newcomers may feel intimidated by the cover girl look when they see their teacher for the first time in class; again, older students might feel more comfortable with an older teacher. It makes perfect sense.

The vast majority of people I come across are 'ordinary' people who want a 'normal' person teaching them. Yes, they want inspiration, to feel invigorated, or 'in the zone', but they want it to come from someone they can relate to as well. That means the qualities they seek in a teacher are not how slim, young, or beautiful they are, but what else they bring to the party, their rapport, empathy, vitality, enthusiasm and knowledge.

In other words, how they make you feel at the end of each session, and how that directs what you do next in your day.

So, fear not, if you're a larger gentleman or lady, or more mature in years, or even with some sort of disability, this is your chance to shine.

Be an inspiration to others, show them what can be achieved, even if you can't touch your toes (heck, even if you have no toes!). Tell me those Olympic wheelchair athletes are not among the most inspiring (and toughest) cookies around. There's nothing they can't do.

Yoga opens up new pathways for all of us. So create your own way. Whatever your shape, size or age, ability or disability, your career path is yours to define.

*Be an inspiration to others,
show them what can be achieved*

YOGA ROCKSTAR TIP #3

'DREAM BIG

"Be accountable to
yourself. If you operate
out of a place of love, you
will get what you give and
perhaps receive more than
you ever dreamed"

Stephanie Spence | USA

Manifest your reality

IF OUR **THOUGHTS** CREATE OUR **REALITY,** THEN LET'S SET ABOUT **CREATING** THE **BEST** POSSIBLE **FUTURE** FOR OURSELVES AND OTHERS

Manifesting your reality is not a scary 'out there' concept for most yogis.

In this great big, unlimited universe of ours, with all that untamed energy swooshing about, we create what we set our sweet little hearts on. Not always - or at least, not always in ways that we can understand or appreciate - but the more you put your focus on something, the more real it becomes.

Warning: if, however, you're working for Big Corporate plc, then the manifesting idea may be less familiar. Try telling the board of an insurance firm that if they just focus twice as hard on doubling their profits all their wildest dreams will come true. It ain't gonna happen.

And so it requires a little leap of faith here.

But science tells us that energy creates energy. You 'attract' what you desire through thoughts, actions, and by placing your energy into this space. Your thoughts themselves are energy.

Think positively and the universe will reflect positivity back to you. Think in negative terms, and yes, you guessed it, the cosmos will respond in kind.

So put your heart and soul into manifesting this new dream life of yours. You want to be a yoga teacher? Then go and be a yoga teacher. Do lots of yoga, read, study and get qualified: that's your path.

You want to be a great yoga teacher, then go and be great. Don't wait for a class to show off your 'greatness' to students; take your yoga greatness wherever you go - yes, to the studio, but also into the high street, into your home, even into how you prepare your evening meal in the kitchen.

Inject yoga into the ordinary and the mundane. Lift people up. Lighten their lives, every step of the way.

Be their inspiration. It will come back to you in swathes of karmic love, adoration and abundance.

Act boldy and powerful forces will come to your aid.

Quick quiz

FAST FORWARD TO YOUR FIRST EVER CLASS

A student comes up to you after your very first class. He (or she) tells you: "That was amazing. I feel so alive. Thank you so much. You are a sensational yoga teacher. I can't wait to come again next week." What's your response?

A: Break down in floods of (happy) tears

B: Say 'thank you' and hug them

C: Jump for joy, kick your heels together and sing hallelujah

Answer: Do all three! Congratulations, you've changed the course of someone's day and, quite possibly, their life. You've created a magical bond with your student.

And, most probably, you now feel a million dollars yourself after doing so.

You are a yoga teacher, my magnificent friend. Welcome to the club.

Hey, you're good at this!

Get inspired

MAKING PEOPLE FEEL GOOD: THAT'S WHAT IT'S ALL ABOUT FOR NEWLY-QUALIFIED INSTRUCTOR, MANDY CARTER

Choose a teacher training course to suit you | I chose to do my training over a year (one weekend a month) because of family commitments. I'm a single mum so it has been tough at times juggling life and finding time to fit in study and an hour's practice every day.

It gets easier with practice | Teaching yoga is very different from being a student. There's so much to remember. Often, when I practice in my living room now I'm talking through the asanas, as it helps to sink in the information.

You do need some confidence | Lesson plans are a must for me although they have to be adaptable and you need to tailor your class to meet your students' needs. Run through it a few times to make sure it works.

I want to share yoga with everyone I'm looking forward to helping people on their yoga journey. I'd like to help single mums in my area and offer them yoga at an affordable price. For mums with little ones to have just an hour of time is incredibly precious. Making people feel good...I love it!

Teaching is very rewarding | It's an amazing feeling when you take a class and you see how much people have relaxed by the end of it. To be a really good teacher I think you have to live and breathe yoga; you have to feel it yourself first

best advice:

Practice everyday and study as much as you can. With knowledge comes confidence and the real 'you' will shine through. It's daunting at first but it gets easier; like a never ending jigsaw with the pieces fitting into place when the time is right.

Mandy Carter UK

Your big blank canvas

PUT YOUR **IMAGINATION** INTO **OVERDRIVE** AND CREATE YOUR OWN **AMAZING** YOGA CAREER PATH STARTING RIGHT NOW

Hands up who's read The Secret? This best-selling book states most eloquently how we can manifest things in our life simply by living and thinking the right way and focusing on all the good stuff. In this way, we start to attract more of what we want in our life, and less of what we don't want. Sounds simple, and it is.

Even improving our mental self-talk, switching to more positive internal mind chatter, can bring about amazing changes. As the great Abraham Lincoln once said: most people are just about as happy as they make up their minds to be.

Things rarely work out exactly as we planned. So let's see if we can get the universe conspiring with us. Get a big artist's sketchbook (or use the space here if you like) and start to draw your future self, your new reality, in as much gorgeous detail as you can. What's the first thing you'll say to your students, in that very first class? Jot it all down.

Vision boards

If you're hopeless at drawing (I am), use a vision board to piece together your new yoga career. Stick a photo of you in the middle, and work your way outwards. Put a yoga class picture next to it so you'll see what you'll look like leading from the front. Scribble down some inspiring quotes. Fill your board with images, messages, anything that propels your dream yoga life forward (think: stunning retreat locations, fab studios, inspiring teachers). You can do this!

Take responsibility

YOU HAVE ALL THE **RESOURCES** YOU NEED INSIDE TO MAKE YOUR **VISION** A REALITY

What you have in your life right now is the result of many factors: an interplay of past decisions, luck (good and bad), your upbringing, social conditioning, emotions, self-belief and self-esteem. This list is pretty much endless.

Here's the good bit though. We can effect change by taking responsibility for ourselves, our decisions, our lives.

Taking responsibility – for what you want in life, for what you do and achieve, for your own happiness even – is one of the most powerful tools we have at our disposal.

If you choose to do nothing you will stay in a state of perpetual stasis. And that's just fine, if that's what you want, it's your call. You are in charge.

On the other hand, if you want to fly, to really soar like an eagle, then that power is within you also. Just take responsibility for it and know that your actions and decisions right now and going forward will greatly direct the course of the rest of your life.

If you really want nothing, then life is pretty easy as you don't have to do anything.

If you want success, however, then you need to take action.

Even this book would never have been written without those two wonderful ingredients: passion and responsibility. Together, these guys are what get things done. Passion is essential, as it brings with it drive, energy and vitality. Personal responsibility brings you the discipline to harness that passion, to see things through and overcome obstacles.

No one else is going to make you a yoga teacher. No one is going to make you a great, or even half-decent teacher, once qualified. Only you can do that. In fact, no one owes you anything.

Take responsibility for all your actions and choices. If you slip up you've only got yourself to blame. What of providence, you ask? Yes, things rarely go to plan, but that's not stopping you from rolling with the punches when things go awry. You have set your intention so plan to see that course of action through.

Life, in all its strange, sometimes maddening ways, will knock you off course from time to time. But you can recalibrate when you need to.

Taking responsibility - for your career, happiness, self-worth - allows you to do this whatever the prevailing winds. It's empowering.

Be empowered. Because you are.

YOGA ROCKSTAR TIP #4
'GET CREATIVE'

"Creative expression
never ceases to amaze
me. Get into the
flow to find your own
inner teacher"

Mercedes Ngoh Sieff | *UK*

show up every day

Do the things you love

FOCUS ON THE GOOD THINGS AND THE GOOD THINGS WILL COME YOUR WAY

If you're still not quite sure what you want out of life then you can at least start to narrow it down a bit.

Here are two questions to help you focus on what you want (and what you don't want). Jot down a few simple answers to get the ball rolling and to start the energy snowball effect. You might want to consider key life areas such as health, personal relationships, career, money and family, but feel free to let your imagination run wild.

A positive intention, no matter how small - if followed with great passion and determination - can lead to monumental things.

Often, when making New Year's resolutions, people over estimate what they can achieve in one single year, but they hugely under estimate what they can do in five years.

Remember: this could be the turning point in your new life.

✔ What do you want to bring more of into your life?

✗ What do you want to bring less of into your life?

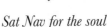

Sat Nav for the soul

Use your emotions to check that you are moving in the right direction, like a kind of emotional Sat Nav. Feeling happy and inspired suggests things are on track. Feeling sad or depressed may mean you've taken a wrong turn somewhere. Don't beat yourself up about it. Check in with yourself from time to time and use these feelings as a guide. What you're aiming for is passion, positivity, energy. No, we can't be 'up' all the time - life is genuinely hard sometimes - but if you're never feeling the vibes then you can address that. Tune in to your intuition.

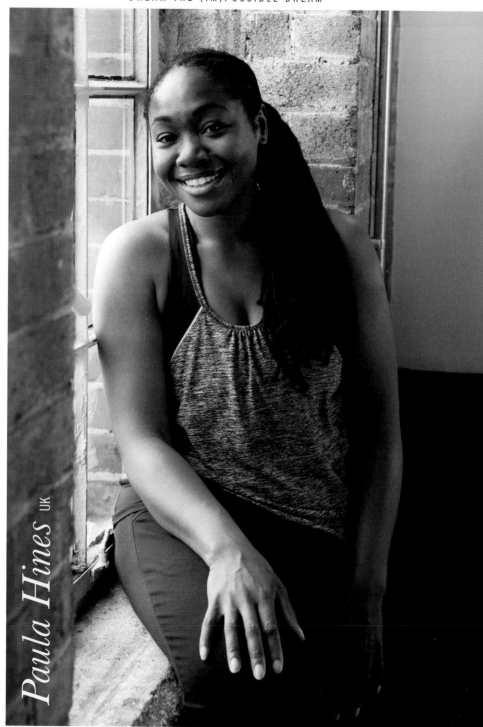

Paula Hines UK

Get Inspired

PAULA HINES WENT INTO YOGA TEACHING AFTER TAKING REDUNDANCY BUT STILL WORKS AS A FREELANCE TV SCRIPT WRITER AND CONSULTANT

Getting started was the hardest part | Working full-time in TV, with a mortgage, and living in London, I couldn't see a way, financially, to make the transition to yoga teaching. Also, deep down, I wasn't sure I could be a yoga teacher because I never saw yoga teachers who looked like me: a short, curvy black woman. Then I was made redundant and I took that as a sign that it was now or never.

The first year was difficult | I was covering classes but had no regular classes of my own. It meant I didn't get to see the same people regularly. The upside, though, was that I became more adaptable, more quickly. Plus I met more people which led to more teaching opportunities.

There are big financial questions Most of my income now comes from teaching, but it has taken three years to get to this point. I still need to supplement my income with other work. With hindsight, a stable income would've taken away a lot of stress. My home is in London where life is expensive, and if I don't work, my bills don't get paid. If you have a full-time job don't quit it for as long as possible, as you build up your teaching work.

best advice:
Just because something is challenging or taking longer than you hoped, doesn't mean you're doing something wrong. And if an opportunity comes up that you can't take, why not make it an opportunity for someone else? What goes around comes around.

Try and be flexible | Once you are teaching, be willing to be flexible and collaborate with other teachers. I now teach a mix of drop-ins, privates, corporates, retreats and on a 200-hour yoga course. Being open to different things can help you find your niche.

Stay true to yourself | Teach what you believe, not what you think you ought to be teaching. Some people will really enjoy your teaching and some people will not. All you can do is your best.

Don't compare yourself to others Don't worry about what others are doing. I hear that teaching yoga - in London, at least - is competitive. I think it's only competitive if you decide it's going to be. I personally don't see it that way. If you work out what you want to do and move in that direction, rather than trying to emulate someone else, then I believe things will work out in the end.

You never stop learning | Most of all, stay open and keep learning. I have learned far more than I imagined since I started out, but I know there's still so much more to learn and there always will be. The thought of that excites me.

The lululemon way

WHO KNEW YOGA FASHIONISTAS LULULEMON WERE ACTUALLY POWERED BY DREAMS?

When you start picturing your new life and cutting out images for your vision board, you'll be in fine company. One of the yoga world's most famous brands, lululemon athletica (you know, the guys that sell the cool pants to pretty much every yogini in the world), is pretty hot when it comes to creating visions and setting goals. The company believes that if you love your life, you will be better at work, better at home, and better at, well, everything really. Here's a step-by-step guide from the nice lululemon folks on how to manifest those dreams of yours.

VISION AND GOALS

Creating a life you love: creating a vision and setting goals is something every lululemon employee does. The aim is to create a vision for your ideal life and to establish goals that allow you to attain it.

THE BIG PICTURE

The 10-year vision: the goal-setting strategy is based on a 10-year vision that includes three core areas: health, personal, and career.

Start by closing your eyes and imagining yourself in 10 years: How old are you? Where do you live?

Who are you with? What have you accomplished? Try not to let yourself be held back by common constraints like time, money and knowledge. Think as big as you can; if you can see it, you can create it.

Write down what you see and what you want. This can be in any form that resonates with you: a story, a moment, a collection of bullet points or a collage of images. Put it all down on paper. Bonus point if what you write inspires you, terrifies you and energises you all at the same time. If that's what you're feeling, you're on the right track.

The intention is to connect you with your future self. Knowing what your vision feels like motivates you to keep moving towards it, even when what you have to do to get there seems hard. The more time you spend uncovering what you really want, the clearer your vision will become. And, by the way, your vision is yours to change at any time.

THE ROADMAP

Goal setting: your goals are the steps you take to achieve your vision; like a roadmap to the life you love.

They are broken down into 10-year, five-year and one-year to help make your long-term vision a reality. Want to sail around the world in 10 years? Plan to take sailing lessons by year five and open a savings account in year one. Start with the 10-year goal that links you to your vision, then trickle back to your goals all the way to year one.

It's important to create balance in these goals by focusing on those three key areas (personal, health, career). Draw three circles on a page, representing these three areas, and define what each of these areas mean to you. For instance, for some people health may include your yoga practice; for others, yoga may be in their career circle.

Remember, balance isn't static: life requires you to make adjustments. What helps is if you're aware of what the things are that restore you and create the balance you seek.

GOALS

When you've completed this it's time to begin to craft, create and set your goals. Be bold and set goals that challenge you. Surprise yourself and have fun with them.

When writing your goals, make sure they are:

Grounded: in your vision and trickle backwards from 10 years to one year.

Specific: order up what you want. When you go to a restaurant you don't order food, you order a salad with the dressing on the side; you ask for what you really want. No hesitations.

Measurable: in order to know you've achieved the goal, you have to be able to measure it in the present tense. State your goals like they're happening.

By when: when will you achieve this goal? This makes you accountable.

The beauty of setting goals backwards from an intentional future is all your focus can be on your one-year goals; this is where all the action happens. The trickle back ensures what you are working on right now matters, engages you and develops into your vision.

THE NEVER-ENDING PURSUIT

The finished product: you've now got a draft of your vision and your goals. Congratulations. It's a big deal to write down what you really want in life, and not what your mum wants or what your partner wants. It's all about you. Now go and share them. Tell the world. This holds you accountable and allows people to support you. Don't wait until they're perfect or comfortable. Share a draft. Post them on the wall, put them up in your bathroom and read them when you brush your teeth. It's reasonable to expect your vision and goals to change as you change. It's a never-ending pursuit that should always be exciting and exhilarating. Be kind to yourself. Make space for discovery. Ask why when you fail. Celebrate when you succeed.

Above all, enjoy creating your life.

Your goals are the steps you take to achieve your vision; like a roadmap to the life you love

More than just yoga pants

NO, YOU'RE NOT JUST A **YOGA** TEACHER: YOU ARE A **CHANGEMAKER**, A **CATALYST**, A **TRUE INSPIRATION** TO ALL STUDENTS

While we're on the subject of yoga pants... a bright young thing from lululemon once told me at the OM Yoga Show in London that inspiring people to create their own visions for their life, and goal setting *(see pages 50-51)*, was what really inspired the company. It's true: the ability to impact peoples' lives is a real gift. And this company has inspired a lot of people.

This person (a qualified yoga teacher) told me that the company sold yoga pants simply to pay for this vision.

I love this attitude.

And it's something any yoga intructor can emulate. No, I don't mean you have to start making and selling your own trendy yoga pants to pursue your own dreams.

Instead, see your work more as inspiring others, transforming lives for the better; to be a touch paper to ignite that spark.

You just happen to sell yoga classes to pay for it.

You really can make a difference to peoples' lives.

And that makes you a very special person indeed.

Time travel for yoga wannabes

HERE'S A **FUN** GUIDE FOR ALL YOU **FUTURE** YOGA **ROCK STARS** OUT THERE

YEAR 1: set the wheels in motion now. Take responsibility to edge closer to your 5-year (and 10-year) goals
★ **Establish yourself as a yoga teacher locally (or at least get qualified to teach)**
★ Get those teaching classes going and the income flowing
★ **Broaden your experience via workshops and retreats**
★ Explore how you might approach those big 10-year targets

YEAR 5: aim to have a platform you can use to achieve your 10-year goals
★ **Grow your reputation, nationally and internationally (if that's what you want)**
★ Activate your social media and marketing presence across multiple platforms
★ **Get those yoga DVDs or online videos made and out to your students**
★ Enjoy seeing yourself as a magazine cover star

YEAR 10: you've arrived. All those years of hard work have paid off

and now you're at the top of your game
★ Headline at Wanderlust in Colorado, or at London's OM Yoga Show
★ **Focus on your teacher trainings, showing the next generation how it's done**
★ Star in your own healthy living yoga and nutrition TV show
★ **Live with abundance in your Malibu beachside apartment**

YEAR 20: heck, you never know what's around the corner, you've got to dream big right?
★ **You are the first yoga teacher to be named president**
★ All wars are over; poverty is a thing of the past. You have brought peace, love and understanding to all continents
★ **People queue up the world over just to give you a hug (oh no, wait, Indian spiritual icon Amma already has that job!)**
★ Your DNA is captured by scientists as the blueprint for yoga teachers of the future and jettisoned into deep space for extra terrestrials to discover
★ **After saving the planet from the brink of destruction you will now rescue the universe.**

How I made it happen

BLISSOLOGY CREATOR EOIN FINN SAYS SOMETIMES IT'S THE NEWEST ACTS THAT TOTALLY ROCK THE JOINT

Eoin Finn CANADA

Yoga is not an individual pursuit | It seems like it is individualistic because we are so quiet on our mats for so long; and we definitely need this time to restore our energy. But what makes yoga so incredible is how it opens up our connection to others. I used to think a great yoga class was about making people sweat, or the sequencing. Now, the ultimate litmus test for an incredible yoga class is when all the barriers between people completely break down and we are all moved by our heart's deepest message of connection.

Success means different things | It's important to define success because yoga is like music. There are plenty of great musicians still dragging their amps on the weekends to local pubs, and plenty of famous musicians filling stadiums who are not so talented. There's an element of drive, luck, natural flexibility, and even good looks, that go a long way to make people successful at teaching yoga.

Be clear on your philosophy | If success is the power to really move people I'd say the most common trait I see is to be clear about what one's core philosophy is; about the intention behind the class. You have to be willing to be vulnerable and believe in what you have to offer and be authentic to this message. You have to stand comfortably naked presenting what lights you up and not be concerned about wearing other people's clothing perfectly.

Try not to compare yourself with others | The main obstacle for new teachers is they tend to compare themselves to people who have been teaching for longer, which causes self-doubt. Again, yoga

fuel your passion

can be like music: sometimes (but not always) it's the newest bands who innovate and bring their passions out confidently. Those that have been around for 20 years are sometimes the ones in a rut, remaking the same sounds every year without the passion. That's not to say there are not established teachers out there teaching masterfully; but new teachers need to know that their freshness and passion can be infectious. I tell all students in Blissology training to feel and repeat this mantra: 'Nothing to prove and evertything to share.'

best advice:

Ultimately, 90% of a class is about sharing positive energy. As long as you're skilled to not injure people with yoga asana, you're in a good position to really light fires in the hearts of the people in your classes. Be confident in that.

3

What makes a great yoga tecaher

"*I am not a woman.*
I'm a force of nature"

Courtney Love

keep it simple

*"The best teachers are
those who show you
where to look, but don't
tell you what to see"*

Alexandra K. Trenfor

True greats

REMEMBER THAT WE ARE ALL STUDENTS, ALL 'BEGINNERS', ON THIS LIFE-LONG YOGA PATH

Some are born great, some achieve greatness, and some have greatness thrust upon them, quoth Shakespeare. It's true. There is no magic formula for achieving greatness in most things in life.

In fact, in yoga, all teachers are great in some unique way.

It may be better to think more in terms of how 'great' your students will feel after your class. If they float off home with big grins on their faces then you're probably on the right track.

But there are some basics to consider too.

Most students will (rightly) assume you have a good understanding of asana, anatomy and physiology. Only with these core skills can you safely instruct individuals on yoga postures or movement, and make adjustments where necessary.

Even here, though, there's always more to learn; science is continually updating ideas on how our bodies work.

So, start by knowing that you do not know everything. Yes, you're a yoga expert, but so too are you a perennial learner and eternal student. Now that's the start point for true greatness.

What the experts say

SO, WHAT DOES MAKE A **GREAT** YOGA TEACHER? HERE'S WHAT A FEW **FAB** YOGA TEACHERS HAVE TO SAY ABOUT IT

"A great yoga teacher is someone who can create a safe space where their students feel inspired and encouraged to explore somewhere inside of themselves they haven't had the courage to explorer before."

Mercedes Ngoh Sieff

"You really need to love yoga and deeply understand it's purpose to be a good teacher. I really feel it's not enough to simply be avle to physically instruct, you need to be embodying the connection that is at it's heart and showing the calm and equanimity that can come from a deep practice in the true, meditative sense"

Charlotte Watts

"A good teacher is a great student first and forever. Recognising your main purpose is very helpful early on, which is to inspire by example."

Duncan Wong

"A great yoga teacher embodies the qualities of humility, integrity, patience, knowledge and humour. They are on the path, working on themselves, so they can be a lighthouse for consciousness."

Katy Appleton

you're amazing

Living your truth

BE YOURSELF AND BE THERE FOR YOUR STUDENTS AND YOU'LL SOON BE THE TALK OF THE TOWN

When it comes down to it, much of being a great yoga teacher is simply about being yourself, or being authentic.

If you can manage this (basically, just act naturally) then your inner beauty and outstanding ability will shine through.

Stay close to the heart, align yourself with good, wholesome yogic ideals (from fair trade and fine, organic food, to charity work) - but without being prescriptive or telling others what to do - and you can't go too far wrong.

Be ethical, be fair, be magnanimous. But don't be pompous.

You already are great, you don't need to do anything to prove it.

Just share that love with all those wonderful students who pay money to come and learn from you.

Always remember: your students are people and individuals with problems of their own; they're not just 'your students' or 'another $10'. You are there to serve them and to support them on their own important yoga journey.

Lift them up, guide and support them - and do it consistently, week in, week out - and you'll soon be the talk of the yoga town.

YOGA ROCKSTAR TIP #5

'STAY POSITIVE'

"Keep a positive attitude
and a desire to help others,
above anything else"

Tara Stiles | USA

Great Teacher Checklist

HERE'S A QUICK CHECKLIST OF **'GREAT** YOGA TEACHER **QUALITIES'** TO MAKE SURE YOU ALWAYS 'SHOW UP' ON THE MAT

1. Be a great student
2. And a good listener
3. Allow students to explore
4. Leave your ego at the door
5. Inspire by example
6. Educate, empower, awaken
7. Get passionate
8. Keep it fresh
9. Remember to have fun
10. And smile!

Mercedes Ngoh Sieff
UK

Get inspired

TAP INTO THAT UNLIMITED POOL OF CREATIVITY TO FIND YOUR OWN UNIQUE TEACHING VOICE

We are all innate teachers | The ability to share what we love, what we know, and what we believe, is in us all. The more we can all tune in to our own inner teacher (regardless of whether you actually teach yoga or not), the more we will be living in union with our higher selves.

Get creative | As a dedicated Vinyasa teacher and teacher trainer, creative expression never ceases to amaze me. Get into the flow to find your own inner teacher.

Appreciate the moment | Over the last 10 years, I have grown increasingly aware of the great magnitude of present moment awareness; to feel, sense and intuit what my students need at any given moment and to teach with a receptive, finely tuned heart. Being truly in and engaged in the moment involves very little planning.

Don't be a slave to your notes
Time and again, I come across a teaching style where the instructor sits in front of the class and refers to a piece of paper and rigidly, almost fearfully, sticks to this plan. If you are fixated on notes you wrote an hour ago (or two weeks ago), you are not engaging with the class in front of you. Somewhere along the way you got lost in the planning and forgot about the moment.

Enjoy the process | Yoga has demonstrated to me a very peaceful and timeless ebb and flow of life, which may sometimes appear stressful, chaotic and intense. But, as long as you remember to tune into the breath, life is a lot more like riding the perfect wave than trying to swim against a strong current. We need only relax, trust and feel the water.

best advice:

Teaching yoga is not about achieving or controlling nor should it be used as a platform to massage your ego. Teaching yoga is more of a calling. It becomes something within you that must be shared in order to be truly integrated, truly understood.

7 steps to greatness

THERE'S NO **MAGIC** FORMULA FOR BEING A **GREAT** TEACHER: JUST BE **YOURSELF**

What are the things you most need to be a fabulous yoga instructor? Sometimes it's not always the most obvious things. Here, Michele Pernetta, a London-based teacher and owner of the Fierce Grace chain of studios, offers her take:

1 A deep desire to help people heal and grow.

2 **A long time regular yoga practice.** If we haven't experienced it ourselves, it is hard to teach it. Being a great yoga teacher comes from having gone through layers of uncovering things in yourself, difficulty and crises, and they deepen your teaching.

3 **A sense of humour.** Humour relaxes us, cuts through ego, and changes us energetically. If a student is straining and effortfully trying to achieve in a pose, a laugh can completely reset the energy and bring them back to the present moment.

be honest

4 **Sensitivity to people's energy.** This sounds a bit new-age but it really isn't. As a yoga teacher you need to be able to read what someone is going through in class. Are they suffering self doubt or too much challenge? Then you can suggest they back off. Are they bored and coasting in their safe place? Then a good adjustment or motivation will reignite their interest. If we can learn to feel and notice what our students are going through, we can tailor our instruction to bring them to the best place for them that day.

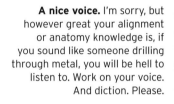

A nice voice. I'm sorry, but however great your alignment or anatomy knowledge is, if you sound like someone drilling through metal, you will be hell to listen to. Work on your voice. And diction. Please.

Be real. There is no need to pretend you are someone you aren't. There's a 'yoga teacher persona' some teachers adopt. Students want to see your humanity, your flaws. Having a perfect, vegan, enlightened teacher, can make students feel they are not good enough, when we are all good enough right now. Don't hide behind any persona. Strip it all away and dare to be who you really are. Only then can you really facilitate others to do the same.

A healthy irreverence. It's very easy to get a bit serious and holier than though, to expound on yoga, veganism or enlightenment in Sanskrit, but this doesn't necessarily help the general public who have struggled into our classes with a bad back, feeling unfit and overweight and who feel out of place as it is. Being able to communicate in accessible human ways, with an understanding of how difficult the beginning of any yoga practice can be, will make our students feel welcome, safe and understood.

Charisma makeover

CONTROVERSIAL? POSSIBLY. DISTASTEFUL? PROBABLY? USEFUL? DEFINITELY!

Not all of us can have the X factor. And thank heavens for that too, or the world would end up like some sort of nightmarish Simon Cowell reality TV production.

We're not all born storytellers, entertainers, or leaders. Most of us are just regular guys and gals.

Still, in our quick-fix culture, where attention spans are measured in nano seconds, you do need to have something about you that will keep your students engaged.

I once attended a class where the teacher (a middle aged man) simply moved from one posture to another, reciting the pages of his yoga manual. He was a really nice guy but it was so dull and uninspiring. I didn't go back.

Of course, you're never going to please everyone, but to give yourself a little extra sparkle it might be worth considering a few things beyond what's in the textbooks.

You may have scored top marks in your anatomy class but if your personality is as flat as a pancake then your true, innate greatness may, alas, go unrecognised and unrewarded. And that is not what we, or you, or the rest of the world, wants.

So here's a quick charisma guide if you're lacking that 'wow' factor:

Deploy atmospheric tools: think subdued lighting or candles for a more mellow, chilled vibe, or even bring in some imagery, or recite poems or inspirational verse. Ambient music is great too. If you're students have just stepped off Main Street then the contrast could not be greater; they'll love it. Instant relaxation.

Self-development: you'll never catch me without some sort of self-improvement or self-help book. Maybe I'm a lost cause but I'm always trying to raise my game in one way or another. Seek out more skills training (public speaking, acting lessons) to help you out, or just browse a bookstore and pick something that'll fire your imagination.

Play to your strengths: maybe your background is in dance, or you love music, so you can incorporate this and put some cool backbeats into your classes. I've heard everything from Bob Marley to The Prodigy used in yoga studios, so anything goes really. Define your style with the help of rock legends. Is it yoga? Who cares? It's your class.

Public speaking for dummies

WE'RE NOT ALL BLESSED WITH CHURCHILL'S ORATORY SKILLS, BUT THAT SHOULDN'T STOP ANY OF US FROM PROGRESSING OUR CHOSEN CAREER WHERE PUBLIC SPEAKING IS CONCERNED

Many newbie yoga instructors have told me that standing up in front of a class for the first time is nothing short of terrifying.

It all boils down to that confidence thing again. They know their yoga, sure enough, but it's more about getting in the zone, and being relaxed enough, to be in a space where they can communicate effectively with their audience (the students). This comes more naturally to some than others.

I've been a best man at two friends' weddings and delivered two speeches. One went spectacularly well, the other was a disaster. I honestly think the difference was down simply to preparation and confidence. I was well rehearsed and ready for the successful one; I was totally unprepared for the other one (which, incidentally, no one ever picked me up on or mentioned, so most of the 'disaster' was probably in my head anyway).

If you struggle with speeches, and the whole idea of standing up in front of a class, just view it as another little skill to acquire, one that you can then toss into your career backpack.

Once you're comfortable, like all other tools you learn along the way, it will help sustain you throughout your entire time teaching. The good news is every single teacher I've ever met says it gets easier the more you do it.

Practice, practice: you should get some practice time during your teacher training course. Make the most of this safe learning space and take on board any feedback you get.

Know yourself: non-verbal presentation is important too, so know how you appear to others. Talk to yourself in the mirror, or video yourself (even if it's painful to watch after). Ask friends and family to be your audience.

Rehearsals: rehearse your instructions or any speech over and over again if you need to. Once it's etched into your brain, it'll be almost second nature; that's one less thing to worry about.

Get passionate: if you're truly engaged with what you're saying then you'll be able to keep your audience's attention far better.

Be kind to yourself: we all mistakes and you will too. Don't beat yourself up when it happens. Speaking in front of others is not easy and it takes time to hone your skills.

YOGA ROCKSTAR TIP #6

'BREAK DOWN BARRIERS'

"The ultimate litmus test
for an incredible yoga
class is when all the
barriers between people
completely breakdown
and we are all moved
by our heart's deepest
message of connection"

Eoin Finn | Canada

go with the flow

Get Inspired

AFTER THE TURMOIL OF A MARITAL BREAKUP, AND A BATTLE WITH DEPRESSION, STEVE JOHANSEN HAS FOUND NEW HAPPINESS THROUGH YOGA TEACHING

Choose your teacher training wisely I spent a long time thinking about what I wanted (content, location, duration). After visiting studios and talking to teachers, my decision was based on how friendly and supportive they were. It was the right thing to do; the friendly ethos nurtured and encouraged me.

Confidence is everything | It's a big deal to step in front of a group of people you don't know, people who are paying you to teach them yoga for the first time, hoping and praying it all goes to plan and that you don't forget anything important.

It won't all go to plan | What you've learned from your teacher training, though, isn't just what the poses are called in Sanskrit or how to get in and out of them safely, it's how to modify them and adapt the class so everyone can enjoy it, especially you.

I got lucky with my first teaching job | If anything, my transition to teaching was easy, but then I think I've been very lucky. Sometimes it's not what you know, but who you know. I was offered a job teaching at a beautiful studio, alongside fabulous people. I've had a lot of jobs in the past, but I've never felt so happy to be a part of this great team.

I want to help more people | I'd like to help people find ways to use yoga to help them deal with depression, not just the symptoms, but some of the more common things that happen in people's lives that contribute to the suffering this mental illness causes. I'd also like to get more men doing yoga.

best advice:

Teach what's in your heart, what you enjoy. Students will pick up on that and enjoy the class too. That way, in time, you'll gain the necessary experience, self-assurance and confidence of a seasoned yoga teacher.

Steve Johansen UK

Alternative careers

THINK OF YOGA **TEACHING** QUALIFICATION AS A PASSPORT TO A MULTITUDE OF **AMAZING** CAREERS

It's hard to think about this prior to even qualifying, but becoming a yoga teacher may not necessarily be an end destination for you.

Yoga really is a lifelong journey of learning.

Your yoga mat, like some sort of flying carpet, can lead you almost anywhere. Literally.

If you really want to get specific in your visions and dreams then you might want to explore some other yoga niches too.

In most cases, these can be viewed more as complementary career choices, perhaps as an additional string to your bow, rather than alternatives. Some are listed here but there are plenty of others too. The reality is that yoga careers tend not to be so linear; it's not like working your way up the corporate career ladder.

Like a monkey flinging itself from one treetop to another, in all directions, it's possible to explore all kinds of different avenues, and at any time. Go where your heart takes you.

If you love yoga, and you have a background of working with children, then it's fairly logical that you might want to combine the two to create

something unique and wonderful.

Here are a few other yoga avenues to explore (there are some more ideas to fire your imagination in chapter 8, on pages 192/193):

Children's yoga teacher: yes, it's challenging (and it can be noisy too), but there can't be many people in the world more fun to work with than kids. If you want to hang out with the future stars of this world, free from inhibition and oozing joy from their very pores, then a career in children's yoga could be for you. From babies and toddlers, all the way through to pre-teens and teenagers, everybody loves yoga.

Yoga therapist: if you're passionate about helping others, especially those with an illness or chronic condition, or you're already from a healthcare background, then yoga therapy could be hugely appealing to you. Already big in the USA, it's also starting to take off in the UK and across Europe. That means plenty of opportunity for new and aspiring teachers.

Meditation coach: not all of us were cut out to be so pliable on the mat. For a lot of people, it's the meditational side of their practice that inspires them to keep coming back for more. With mindfulness meditation now in the mainstream, it's something that's likely to grow in popularity as people seek some mind calm in this crazy world. And that means this planet of ours will need more meditation guides to help us find that illusive inner peace.

Spiritual musician: yogis are a creative bunch, you know. You don't have to go far before finding one strumming on a guitar or banging on the bongos. There's a huge demand for soft, soulful, spiritual music to uplift the millions of practicing yogis out there, and there's always a requirement for new material. Plenty of good yoga rock stars out there already too if you're seeking some inspiration. Do

a bit of research to find out how they made it happen.

Studio owner: many yoga studio owners are not actually yoga instructors at all, just individuals looking to create an inviting place of healing and wellbeing for the benefit of others. If you love yoga but don't want to go down the traditional teacher training route, then the idea of studio ownership might be appealing. Bring that yoga vibe to all without teaching a single class. Great for those with a business mind.

PR & media: again, you don't even need to have taught a class for this, but many instructors go on to help others (celebrity teachers, studios, other yoga entities) with marketing and public relations support. If you've got some media background, and you love yoga, then you're halfway there.

"A yoga teaching qualification can also be a passport to many other types of amazing work opportunities"

How I made it happen

KATY APPLETON HIT THE BIG TIME EARLY IN HER CAREER AFTER TEAMING UP WITH A FORMER SPICE GIRL

I've had so many career highs | Creating two yoga DVDs with a celebrity (former Spice Girl Geri Halliwell) that sold over half a million copies worldwide. That carved the way for writing two books and creating more DVDs over the years. Five years ago I created the appleyoga academy, offering a variety of teacher training courses – watching these grow, and the teachers who have passed through them, has been so exciting.

I have a very strong work ethic | Keep working hard and you will see the results and fruits of your labour appear.

The business of teaching yoga has changed | It's a mainstream, big bucks business worldwide. Many more hybrid forms of yoga are appearing, offering an 'in' for the many different people who show up. More people seem to be interested all the time, so the global shift of consciousness is moving at a faster rate – something that's so needed for our planet.

Be humble, be authentic and be present | Really live the journey, not just in the yoga room. Keep working on your own journey of unravelling, considering and transformation to truly teach. Try to work on seeing every person as fundamentally good, even in the most challenging moments. Own your shadow too; we all have one.

Katy Appleton UK

best advice:

Be present, honest and authentic; stay compassionate and committed. Shine bright whenever you hold space in the yoga room.

#4

Teacher Training

accept change

"*If I feel comfortable with what I'm doing, something's wrong*"

David Bowie

*Courage is
a choice*

mistakes happen

First things first

BEFORE YOU TAKE
ON THE **WORLD**
YOU'LL NEED TO
TAKE **CARE** OF A
FEW DETAILS FIRST
– LIKE GETTING
QUALIFIED

LISTEN UP SUPERSTAR: before you book your flight to the Maldives to host your first ever yoga retreat in paradise you'll need to take care of a few details first - like getting qualified.

Getting certified to teach is the first concrete step to making a career out of doing what you love.

It's pretty important too. You'll struggle to get insurance or teach at gyms if you can't show the right bits of paper to your prospective employer.

After all, you wouldn't fancy taking part in a class where the teacher doesn't know his bottom from elbow would you?

PICK YOUR PATH
But it can be confusing too with so many options and alternatives out there.

For starters, there are so many accreditation bodies, each offering different qualifications. And that all varies immensely from one country to another.

Make sure you do your research to get the one that works best for you. That will vary depending on what sort of career you're planning. Similarly, your training path might be determined by the style of yoga you follow. Different rules apply, for instance, if you're planning to be a Kundalini yoga teacher or an Iyengar instructor (which typically takes a lot longer).

Confusing huh?

YOGA ROCKSTAR TIP #7
'TEACH WHAT YOU LOVE'

"Teach what you believe,
not what you think you
ought to be teaching"

Paula Hines | *UK*

respect all others

What to look for in a teacher training course

DON'T BE AFRAID TO **ASK QUESTIONS** BEFORE YOU SIGN UP TO A TEACHER TRAINING

There are so many teacher training courses to choose from, most (but not all) being run by wonderful, talented and exceptional people.

Here, your choice may well need to be determined by personal preference as well as the type of yoga style being offered.

Pick a teacher that resonates with you, one that you work well with and that understands you; most of all, pick someone you really like.

Look around and don't be afraid to ask questions. Lots of quetions.

Think about things that might not immediately spring to mind as well, like what sort of support you get after the course, including practical help in starting and running your own business. It could make all the difference if you want to make a career out of this in the long-run.

Other factors to consider include the duration and structure of a course, as well as the location.

It may sound great spending a month in Hawaii for an intensive training but can you really afford to give up your day job?

Perhaps it makes more sense for you, because of personal circumstances, to spread the training over a longer period of time, maybe as long as three years, so that you can incorporate it more comfortably into your everyday life.

And, of course, getting the right professional qualification is another essential to teaching. This can be confusing, however. Be sure to check out who's who in the yoga accreditation world, which varies from country to country.

If there's a studio you admire, and you dream of one day teaching there, ask the boss what it would take to be able to do that. Then go in the direction of that path.

Do your research

LOOK AROUND AND FIND A TEACHER THAT REALLY RESONATES WITH YOU PERSONALLY

This is one big crucial bit. Consider who you'd like to train with. First, go to lots of classes and ask teachers that inspire you who they take their inspiration from. As well as sound yoga knowledge, other qualities, like being attentive and compassionate, can be important. You'll be spending a lot of time under your instructor's guidance so make sure you don't feel intimidated by them.

Think about how much time you want to spend training and where. Trainings vary in length, from one month to three years. Will you be able to incorporate that training into your regular life? Yoga teacher training is definitely an investment, meaning you'll want to get something out of it in the end, whether that's a deeper understanding of yourself, or an alternative means of earning a living. Hopefully both.

A useful way of exploring the multitude of teacher training options out there is to attend a yoga show or festival, where you can get a feel for all the different schools and styles in the space of just one day. Look out for free mini taster sessions with well-known teachers. It means students can get a feel for what a teacher training course might be like without making any real commitment.

SELF REFLECTION

Rather like an actor, the role of yoga teacher requires a strong understanding of self in order to speak with clarity, knowledge, truth and humility. Check that your training spends some time on self-reflection. You may not like what comes up but it's a step to transformation. With your own self inquiry practice you can offer greater support to your students and still maintain healthy boundaries. It means you'll be better able to tap into students' needs before they even know it. Regular inner house cleaning (both during and after training) will also reveal your true strength of character.

It'll be so much easier if you have an understanding teacher who you can communicate openly with on your course, someone that resonates with you personally.

hug trees

Get inspired

AFTER TRAINING AS A BARRISTER, AMY COOP FOLLOWED HER YOGA DREAM TO BALI

I was nervous before the course
I'm naturally shy and although yoga is the antithesis of competition, I did worry my 10 years of practice might be inadequate compared to the rest of the group. It turned out I was very wrong. My fellow trainees became my extended family and their compliments about my practice made me very humble and gracious.

Be prepared for transformation
The highlight for me was the spiritual journey and the people I connected with. It opened up something amazing in me and I'm inspired by a world of possibility. The hardest part was waking up to this realisation. Never before have I cried during Savasana.

Teacher training is just the start
My course set me up foundationally to start teaching right away, especially considering my long term practice, however, I do feel that I would benefit from studying advanced modules with more of my favourite teachers.

More sequencing please | We were
taught in the format of learning a set sequence to teach, but I wasn't really a fan of that. We were taught in the format of learning a set sequence to teach, but I wasn't really a fan of that. Although we learned how to safely teach a number of common yoga poses and some amazing adjustments, a minimal part of the course covered sequencing. This is a huge interest of mine. I love the creativity and therapeutics involved, as well as the ability to personalise my own yoga classes and more content and support on this subject would've been incredibly beneficial to me.

Things are going great | Everything is
going better than I ever imagined since the course. I now teach three classes a week on top of my legal day job. It's been so rewarding. In hindsight, I think my teacher training set me up perfectly, and I've found where I'm supposed to be. I've now signed up for prison yoga teacher training in Amsterdam, something I am keenly interested in.

best advice:
I came home tired, sore and having spent all of my money but I don't regret a thing. If your whole heart and soul are singing for you to do this, then take the plunge.

Amy Coop UK

Ask the teacher

WHAT DO YOU **THINK** THIS IS: 20 **QUESTIONS?**
(WELL, ACTUALLY, YES IT IS!)

There's a dizzying array of teacher training options out there. Make sure you ask the right questions - and get all the answers you need - before you sign up to anything. Here are some things you might want to ask first:

HISTORY:
★ How long has the school been established?
★ How many students/graduates do they have?
★ Can you talk to some of their former students?
★ How many of their graduates are now actually teaching?

CERTIFICATION:
★ What qualifications will you receive at the end of the course?
★ Who is the course accredited with?
★ How qualified are the instructors?
★ Will the qualification/course be recognised by insurance providers?
★ How much contact will there be with the lead trainer?

PRACTICAL:
★ Where is the course held?
★ How big are the class groups?
★ How long does the training last?
★ Are there flexible payment options or early bird discounts?
★ What's the structure of the course (weekends, intensives, five-day modules)?
★ Is there a practical teaching component on the course?

SUPPORT:
★ What support do they offer their yoga teachers after the course?
★ Do they offer any postgraduate training?
★ Any practical support available for building your own business?

OTHER:
★ What makes their course different from all others?
★ Do they have specialists in other relevant fields (osteopathy, medicine, sports science) on the teaching team?

tread lightly

An investment in you

A TEACHER TRAINING COURSE IS AN **INVESTMENT** IN YOUR **FUTURE** NOT JUST A NICE **HOLIDAY**

And then there's the cost. Expect initial teacher trainings to cost anything from around £1,000 to £3,000, so this is very much an investment in you and your future.

Try not to be seduced by glamour locations ahead of the curriculum. You'll be working hard throughout your training so even if you are lucky enough to be able to spend a month in some Far Eastern paradise it won't be a walk in the park. There's nothing wrong with jetting off to some place wonderful to do your training - there's probably nothing better, in fact - provided the course gives you precisely what you are looking for.

You'll be worked hard by your tormentor (I mean, teacher!): think early morning starts, yoga history texts, anatomy classes and exams, rather than beaches, sangria and sightseeing.

If it's do-able, then by all means pack your suitcase and jet off somewhere lush for the experience. Just don't expect to live on Easy Street when you get there.

Don't be fooled. Yoga teacher training is no picnic. Yes, an exotic location will make break times all the more special, scoffing your pumpkin seeds as the ocean waves lap the shore - the whole trip is likely to be one of the most memorable times of your life, in fact - but expect to work hard, with little play in-between. There's no easy route to qualification. As the old saying goes: you can run, but you can't hide.

So worth it

There's no substitute for following your dreams and doing what you truly love. A teacher training course is not a holiday; it's hard work. So expect some aches and pains along the way, plenty of self-analysis, a few tears, and some inner exploration too. It may well bring up difficult issues and emotions for you too, so be ready for this.

And there's more: yoga teacher training gulps a large amount of time so make sure you're ready to scale back your social life for a while (no more DVD boxsets for a while!). At the end of it all, though, it's likely you will have had one of the most memorable times of your life, making friends, learning new skills and, ultimately, getting ready to take your new craft out into the world. A whole new life awaits...

YOGA ROCKSTAR TIP #8

'STAY ON THE PATH'

"It's important to stay on
your yogic path so you can
be the best version of you
to help your students find
the best versions of them"

Paige Held | *USA*

dance your socks off

Forget comfort zones

BE PREPARED TO **PUSH** YOUR **BOUNDARIES** DURING YOUR TEACHER TRAINING COURSE

Yoga teacher training is no easy ride. And everyone makes mistakes or struggles at some point. Here are some of the things that may await you:

★ That 'back to school' feeling can be strange for those that have not studied anything for years. Any good yoga course will include a decent level of study and homework. So be prepared to knuckle down to some hard work.

★ You'll be amazed how much of your time yoga teacher training gulps. This is a real commitment you're making so be ready for it and it's impact on other areas of your life.

★ Expect a few aches and pains in your body after such an intense period of yoga development.

★ Physical stuff aside, yoga training could also affect other areas of your life; these will be easier to spot and manage if you're expecting possible change and are receptive to it.

★ Similarly, going through an intense period of self-reflection and development you should expect some 'issues' with new emotions rising to the surface. Know that it will come and know that it will pass.

★ During the course you might feel inadequate at some point, and not 'good enough' to be a yoga teacher. This is perfectly normal; just roll with it. You are good enough.

Sarah Jane Griffiths UK

best advice:

Don't be overwhelmed by the sheer number of courses out there. Get on YouTube and do some classes. Look around for a yoga instructor that inspires you and strikes a chord.

Get inspired

COUNTRY GIRL AND ASPIRING HEALTH COACH, SARAH JANE GRIFFITHS, DITCHED THE WELLIES TO TRAIN WITH 'YOGA REBEL' TARA STILES IN NEW YORK CITY

Don't compare yourself to others | My main fear before my teacher training course was not being flexible enough. But, as they say, 'comparison is the thief of joy', so I was determined not to let this ruin my time. I just focused on my own moves and I soon learned that flexibility begins in the mind.

I want to keep on learning | I'm now looking forward to developing as a yoga instructor and finding ways of combining this with other training such as weight-bearing classes (I'm a fitness instructor also) to help people get a great body and mind combined.

My goal is a health coaching business | I hope to inspire people to eat well, chew well, breathe well, crave less and have more zest for life. I believe that if a person can work on their relationships, career, physical fitness and finding a spiritual path, then their life will be more balanced, juicy and joyful.

Think about your future career | I'm going to let it all unfold but I have determination to make it work. All I know is I want to be shaped by what I love not by what I think I should be.

I don't want to pigeon-hole myself It's not just about food and exercise: career and relationships are nutrition too, and no amount of green juice is going to make you happier if these areas are making you miserable. I see myself with a thriving health coaching business, with yoga as an integral part, to help people connect back to their bodies and start believing in themselves again.

There's no one size fits all | Not everyone will enjoy yoga to music or the fact that we don't chant or use Sanskrit but there will be those that do, and that's all that matters. Ultimately, if you leave your mat happy, relaxed and haven't looked at the clock, then my job is done.

Alana Littler & Heather Cereghino

FOUNDERS OF CLOVER PR, A CONSCIOUS PR FIRM
IN SOUTHERN CALIFORNIA

IF YOU GOT INTO YOGA FOR THE LOVE OF THE PRACTICE
AND ARE JUST STARTING OFF IN AN OVER-SATURATED
MARKET, THE CHANCES ARE YOU DON'T HAVE A HUGE
BUDGET TO DEDICATE TO MARKETING YOURSELF. HERE
ARE A FEW EASY TIPS TO GET YOU GOING:

GO MOBILE

Join mobile apps that market your classes, workshops and
retreats for free.

A great example is FindMyYogi, which allows you to upload
your profile, posts your classes and alerts students of any
schedule changes or additions in real time.

GET SOCIAL

Most mindful yogis don't find dedicating hours a day on social
media to be their favourite way of marketing themselves. But it's
an integral part of getting your name out there. The trick? Make
your time count and be strategic.

Search for, follow and engage yogis and studios that resonate
with you on Instagram. This will help increase a valuable following
for you. Find yoga Twitter chats like 'Yoga Chat' online. Then join
in to connect with other yogis and students and to grow your
own social and studio following.

FRIEND-A-MENTOR

Follow in the footsteps of those yogis you respect most. If not the
teacher you studied under, then connect with a local yogi who
has similar methodologies and a strong following.

Invite them to coffee after class and ask how they got their
start. They'll give invaluable insights about how they got started,
and who knows...once they've heard about your style and your
practice, maybe they'll call you next time they need a sub.

Building confidence

IT TAKES **TIME** TO GAIN **CONFIDENCE,** BUT HAVING THE **RIGHT** TEACHER CAN HELP

Getting class confident takes time and experience. It's all too common to find newly-qualified teachers having sleepless nights at the thought of taking that first class.

Late night class planning, nerves' it's all part of the game. It certainly helps if you've had a thorough training that includes plenty of hands-on, practical teaching work. After all, practice makes perfect.

It's hard to teach from just reading a text book - as any high school teacher dealing with teenagers will tell you.

Luckily, you don't have to be perfect. You'll never please everyone; you'll never be all things to all people.

Find that authentic voice, the one that reflects your interpretation and understanding of yoga, and don't even bother to appeal to allcomers.

Not everyone will like you or your class style, so don't be disheartened by that fact; that's just life.

If you are able to connect with others on that genuine level though then most will at least appreciate your authenticity, and you'll probably find a lot of students coming your way.

Likewise, don't even bother comparing yourself to others if they seem more bendy or confident than you. That's just the way it goes.

Maybe you can do certain things they can't. It does not indicate that they - more than you - should be pursuing a teaching career or qualification. Each and every one of us has unique skills and abilities and that's what makes our planet so incredibly beautiful.

So don't be afraid to make mistakes. On a training course, you're in the perfect place to screw up, it's all just a part of the learning process. A supportive environment in your teacher training course will be a major benefit here.

A lot of this also boils down to what sort of person you are. If you're naturally confident, you may have the resilience to simply brush off those mistakes.

If you tend to get demoralised quickly then you may need to work on this side of your game. But this is a transformational experience on so many levels and, with the right teacher to guide you, you'll take away so much more than a certificate at the end of it all.

Continuous Professional Development

THE NEED TO KEEP **LEARNING** YOUR **CRAFT** IS IMPERATIVE IF YOU'RE TO STAY AT THE **TOP** OF YOUR **GAME**

Even after your course, the learning never really ends for a true yoga instructor. For any established teacher, the idea of continuing professional development (CPD) will already be quite familiar, but maybe less so for newcomers.

It's simple. Just as any good doctor needs to brush up on the latest medical science and procedures, so too do yoga instructors need to familiarise themselves with new teaching trends in key areas such as anatomy and physiology.

Indeed, some form of CPD obligations are common to most professions the world over, in medicine, the law, accountancy and architecture.

Within the yoga world, this typically follows the completion of formal teacher training. It can consist of any educational activity that helps to maintain, develop or grow knowledge, problem-solving, technical skills or professional performance standards.

And at the end of these 'mini courses' you (typically) get a nice certification that raises your experience level, and your standing among your peers.

In this way, teachers are then able to provide better standards and, ultimately, better yoga classes, a situation in which everyone stands to benefit.

Teachers, by continuing to work on their training and qualifications, are able to offer more innovative instruction, sequencing or skills and therefore are able to reach students on new levels. And let's face it, students deserve to be receiving the very best instruction possible.

BUSINESS CASE

And it all makes good business sense too. If you're looking to establish yourself as a commercially viable yoga teacher,

invest in you

you'll need to be constantly updating your skills and increasing the depth of your knowledge through CPD. In fact, it's something that could mean the difference between getting insured or not.

Still, if you're in this for the love of yoga it's not so much of a problem. It's an added benefit to the job, if anything, since you'll be learning new things within a subject that you're already passionate about anyway.

And this learning could be scattered across a wide range of areas from sequencing and lesson planning, through to professional studies or meditation.

NEW DIRECTIONS

There are so many CPD options. It may include studying thousands of years of yoga history; or ayurveda, yoga's sister science; or healthy nutrition, raw food or vegetarianism; maybe the Sanskrit texts; or even other esoteric areas that some teachers include in their classes and workshops.

Yoga classes are typically inspired by the self-practice of the teacher standing at the front of the class, so it's vitally important to retain that student mindset at all times. It's a common theme running throughout this book.

Teachers have to expose themselves, therefore, to the masters in their fields, from in-depth asana studies, through to areas that might include yoga business planning, or even just super popular teachers that will inspire them on to new heights.

Whatever route you take, CPD is something you cannot afford to ignore if you plan on making this a long-term career choice.

MAKING CONNECTIONS

The need to keep on learning your craft is important in other respects too.

CPD exposes teachers of all levels to other like-minded peers, experts, and other sources of information.

This helps build connections and stimulates discussion, ideas and knowledge sharing, which can be a rich source not only for self improvement but also for career progression.

This level of personal contact can also play a big role in shifting teachers forward if they become 'stuck'. It's all too easy to become complacent, to get stuck in a rut or a routine, without intervention or the input and interaction of others with fresh ideas.

In this sense, CPD is an opportunity to see new perspectives, and to gain new vision. Moreover, it's all about confidence building. Think about modules in areas like yoga therapy, which is gaining huge traction nowadays in the West as an aid to people with all manner of illnesses.

The scope for further education in this area alone is almost limitless, since you are effectively venturing into the medical and healthcare realm. There really is always something else to learn.

It's true in yoga and it's most definitely the case in healthcare too.

CPD in this sense is merely a further investment in you and your career (okay, yes, it's also a great excuse to go and enjoy some fabulous workshops with some amazing and brilliant teachers that you admire).Nothing wrong with that.

How I made it happen

Guru Jagat USA

KUNDALINI ROCK STAR GURU JAGAT SAYS IT'S ALL ABOUT HARD WORK AND STAYING TRUE TO YOUR PRACTICE

I've had some big career moments | Studying with Yogi Bhajan (blessing me with my name, and teaching at his original Kundalini yoga school in LA, Yoga West) before he passed. And then getting the transmissions once he passed to open RA MA Institute.

The business of teaching yoga has changed
It's now a multi-billion dollar industry, which means people are now, more than ever, putting a value on their health and wellness.

Always stick to your values and core truths
Dedication to your teacher, your lineage and your practice are crucial, first and foremost. Don't get caught up in some marketing or fame game.

Don't be afraid of hard work | My East Coast work ethic has been my greatest gift in my career. I'm not afraid to put in the hours.

You need a mix of competencies | Devotion, commitment to practice (on and off the mat), meditation and hard work.

best advice:

*Focus on your deep devotion and
meditation as a yogi so that you actually
have something to transmit of value to
your students. Serve others and everything
else will come to you in the most
profoundly prosperous way.*

5

Starting out

why wait?

"*As a rock star, I have two instincts,
I want to have fun, and I want
to change the world*"

Bono

Good things come to those who hustle

Anais Nin

Congrats, you're a yoga instructor

BE **PREPARED** TO PUT IN SOME **LEGWORK** IF YOU WANT A LONG-TERM CAREER

So, you've graduated from teacher training with flying colours and you want to start building your new career.

LEARNING THE ROPES

For most people, this is a time of learning the ropes, setting up classes of their own, working out what content to include and, crucially, attracting students. It can also mean providing cover for more established yoga teachers in your area as a substitute (or 'sub'). This is a popular route into the world of paid yoga teaching.

How you go about all of this will depend on what you want to achieve and, of course, where you live. Your choices will be more abdundant in the big cities but, while there may be plenty of yoga outlets, competition will also be more intense.

Some are happy to teach anywhere and everywhere, from church halls to cruise liners. Others may have more set ideas: they only want to do their own thing or teach inside one of the town's top studios.

Wherever you're heading, you'll most likely have to put in lots of legwork.

There's typically no shortcut to long-term success.

Business support

Hopefully, by now, you will have gained some valuable teaching insight from your course. In fact, if you chose wisely, you may even receive ongoing business support from your course provider as you step into the world of paid teaching (this is a great thing to look out for before you actually sign up). Any expert help in areas such as marketing, websites and bookkeeping can be invaluable at this early stage.

YOGA ROCKSTAR TIP #9

'FIND YOUR SPACE'

"Do a bit of research and find a catchment area that isn't already served by regular teachers. This is both to give your own business a chance to flourish, but also to practice respectful ethics towards other teachers"

Charlotte Watts | *UK*

Taking your first steps

MAKE SURE YOU'VE GOT A FEW **MARKETING** **BASICS** IN PLACE BEFORE YOU BEGIN

When you're ready to go out into the 'real world', and teach yoga for money, then it's helpful to have a few basics in place like business cards and a website.

This doesn't have to be anything fancy, but it must announce your presence to the world. A simple site allows you to be found by potential students in your area.

Think of it more as a virtual business card, stating how to get in touch with you (your name, phone, email, yoga style).

With simple online web-building packages now available you may be able to build your own site yourself. If not, recruit someone to do it for you. If you can't afford that, then offer free yoga classes in return for developing the site.

However, if you're more tech-savvy then the online world is your oyster when it comes to marketing.

This opens up other online social media possibilities (such as Facebook and Instagram, although you don't have to have a website for these, just an email address). These are incredible free tools for building community and letting people know that you're out there and what you're up to. It makes you visible and accessible.

Don't forget Old School ploys too: get some flyers printed (or do them yourself at home) and place them on community boards, at local gyms, schools and village halls, anywhere you think students might be looking.

Make contact with any studios in your area and introduce yourself. It doesn't pay to be shy especially in the early days; it could lead to opportunity.

GET CREATIVE TOO

Find ways to approach new groups. For example, if a study shows that police officers are under too much stress, try pitching a stress reduction course to the local police department.

Think outside the box. If you are trying to drum-up interest in one of your early classes, be sure to tell all, including the local press.

Ask as many other teachers as you possibly can to see how they got started. Listen to them. Take notes.

Then follow your own path. This is your story to write, no one else's.

Every successful yoga teacher did it their way; there's no set formula when it comes to getting established.

Above all, be clear and authentic, as this will help you win through in the end. It may be difficult establishing yourself during these first few months (and years) but it can be done.

Lots of others have done it before you.

Paying the bills

IF YOU WANT TO DO THIS LONG-TERM YOU'VE GOT TO **START THINKING** 'MONEY'

Okay, this is is where things get tricky. It's also why one of the first things mentioned in this book was about NOT giving up the day job. (What do you mean you quit already?)

The financials of yoga teaching can be tough. It will vary enormously, of course, depending on your personal circumstances and expectations, where you live and, to some degree, how much of a go getter you are.

How well supported you are in these early years - with a job, through your understanding partner, or by a rich sugar daddy - makes a huge difference.

Let's assume, for now, you need to earn as much as possible, as quickly as you can, in order to pay the rent.

Remember that if you're working for yourself and teaching is your sole source of income then you need to teach - and you need to teach a lot.

At the start, you might need to average over a dozen classes per week to break even, maybe more, maybe less, depending on where you are and what rates you can command. It also depends how much you need to earn to first break even and then, after that, live a little.

Even then, how much you make will depend on studio numbers and many other factors.

During the busiest times you should aim to be making more so you can ride out the less busy times more comfortably. But student class numbers are so hard to predict. A great clss size for you to earn some decent money at a busy studio might be 25 students.

Sadly, I've been to all too many classes where the numbers can be counted on just one hand (in fact, sometimes just one finger).

It means pay can be erractic and unpredictable. Not helpful when you need to pay the bills.

Either way, in order to get close to full-time teaching - and giving up that day job (if that's your dream) - you'll need to put in a lot of hours, do a lot of chasing new business, and cosying up to a lot of students and studio owners.

Get Inspired

WHEN FIRST STARTING OUT, KATHLEEN STAVERT SAYS IT'S IMPORTANT TO BE OPEN TO EVERY OPPORTUNITY THAT COMES ALONG

Get to know lots of teachers
I worked in a yoga studio and was lucky enough to know a lot of teachers who soon began asking me to cover their classes. I said yes to every cover I could take even if it was the other end of the city.

Make yourself known | If you don't know many teachers, go to classes and introduce yourself; get their business cards and write to them to offer yourself up for cover. Established teachers are always looking for someone to cover their class.

My classes soon built up | I teach on average 10-11 classes a week and about half of those I got through covering first. Now I probably cover three or four times a month.

Say yes to opportunity | Visit studios in your area, offer their staff a taster and keep following up. Say yes to opportunity, but stay mindful. In saying yes to everything, you may end up taking on classes all over the place and the travel will probably be the most exhausting aspect of your teaching.

Polish up your class plans | Always have a class plan for the week with modifications for different levels. You may theme your class from your own practice, or something you wish to cultivate in your own life such as balance or accepting change; create your sequences around this theme. My training had a great module on class planning - make sure yours does too.

Always be prepared | Adopt a boy scout motto and be prepared. Even the best teachers spend quality time each week prepping their classes.

best advice:

I say this from experience: say yes until you need to say no. Look after yourself first and be mindful of your energy levels. You'll be giving a lot of yourself, so you'll need to be well rested and healthy.

Kathleen Stavert CANADA

See the OM in 'O-My-God!'

PUT THINGS IN **PERSPECTIVE** AND **LAUGH** IT OFF WHEN THINGS GO AWRY

We all make mistakes. We are all human.

When you are teaching you will not always give the best instruction; occasionally you will be tired and you will mistake your left arm from your right leg.

Especially when covering for a very popular or experienced teacher, you might start to fumble your words or get flustered.

It may result in an 'Oh my God, what am I doing?' moment.

If that happens, take a step back, breathe, and try and laugh it off. Chances are your students will laugh too and the mood in the room will brighten.

Always remember you are a yoga teacher, teaching a yoga class - you're not on the UN Security Council voting for military intervention in some far-off world hotspot.

This is not to undermine the power of your position as a teacher but rather to reinforce it. It's okay to laugh at yourself, acknowledge your mistakes and keep going. Your students will appreciate that you are human and are only too happy to show your flaws. Surprisingly, this levity encourages people to open up as well. Your class then becomes a ground for transformation and mutual learning – and some good ol' fashioned fun.

Now that's what makes a fabulous teacher.

First night nerves

DON'T SWEAT IT WHEN IT'S YOUR FIRST **CLASS,** YOU'RE GONNA BE JUST **FINE**

It's your first class. You break out in a cold sweat at the thought of it.

But this is why you're here, so you need to handle it. And guess what... you will.

Still, these feelings are only natural when embarking on any new venture. And its no different stepping out to lead your very first yoga class.

Maybe you're suffering from imposter syndrome, or you feel like a fraud?

Are you the image of that perfect yogi or yogini? Probably not. Will the people see right through you?

Do you think everyone is waiting on your every word, to deliver deep and meaningful spiritual insight, or pitch perfect anatomical instruction?

AM I GOOD ENOUGH?

Relax. A bit of self doubt is natural. Just go with the flow. Be honest with your students. If you don't know the answer to a question, own up and admit it. Students will appreciate the honesty.

It helps to plan as much as you can, as this then builds a degree of confidence, and allows for greater spontaneity. But know that you're not alone in this. Those very human qualities of fear, insecurity and vulnerability, these are things we all encounter at some point, whether you're a yoga instructor or an oil driller.

It will get easier, for sure. Even the most experienced teachers still face these issues from time to time.

American yoga superstar Kathryn Budig once admitted her initial terror when fellow yoga icon Seane Corn stepped into her class for the first time.

You know what happened? Her esteemed student came back again and again for more. Now that's a real vote of confidence.

And (confession alert here) as a new journalist starting out, years ago, it was not unknown for me to shake at the prospect of conducting big interviews (like Nelson Mandela). I may have looked a little silly, but people are (mostly) kinder than our fears suggest. And, in the end, life moves on anyway.

It's all good.

The confidence to teach

DON'T ALLOW **CONFIDENCE** ISSUES TO BLOCK YOU FROM ACHIEVING YOUR **DREAMS**

This was discussed in the previous chapter but it's worth re-visiting now you're ready to step out onto the real-life studio stage.

As in all walks of life, confidence is pretty darn important when it comes to yoga teaching. I've seen 'em all: bullet-proof teachers with unshakable confidence, as well as timid beginners.

Yes, confidence is essential, but it comes through in different ways for different people. Naturally confident people, even those inclined to arrogance, may have no problem here, but that doesn't mean they will automatically be the best teachers. Other qualities, like empathy, honesty and charm, are super important too.

Those that struggle with confidence may feel that they have to fake it, but here's the thing: yes, that first class may be terrifying, but if you're teaching from the heart, from a place of true authenticity, then that natural approach will ultimately shine through.

I'd pick humble and honesty over a big gob anyday.

You most certainly do not need to be arrogant, just take control and lead from the front; over time, that confident edge will take root. Just be you.

If you really suffer from terrible nerves, then maybe tailor your approach to smaller classes, or get comfortable first by leading groups of friends. It's all good experience.

Sell yourself

Here's the bottom line though when it comes to showcasing your talents at a big studio: students and studio owners don't want an average or shy teacher.

If you have confidence in your practice and you believe that you are great at sharing it with others, and you are sure you deserve a class at that busy studio, show that to whoever needs to see it.

Invest your money to practice often at studios where you want to teach. Roll your mat down close to the teacher. Thank the instructor after class for that great adjustment. If you're comfortable enough, let the teacher or owner know that you

completed your training and would love to get on the sub list. Show yourself off, sell yourself. In the end, it's a business. If you don't take advantage, someone else will.

And (yet another confession alert here) as a new journalist starting out, years ago, it was not unknown for me to mimic the style of another writer, or even lift the odd clever turn of phrase now and then. Ahem. Enough said.

The message: it may feel disingenuous at first, but don't worry about it, you're just a rookie learning your trade. There's plenty of time to develop that uniqueness that undoubtedly lies within.

Keep it simple

MORE STARTING OUT TIPS

(COURTESY OF MIAMI-BASED INSTRUCTOR BETHANY PLATANELLA)

1 **Have a home practice.** You will always have a flow to start with or fall back on.

2 **If you don't have a home practice,** find one or two teachers you admire and attend their classes as often as you can. Your mind and body will memorise the flow, and this can be used as your base.

3 **Ignore the fluff until you are comfortable.** Inhale, right foot forward, Warrior 1. This is enough to start. The students only really need to hear the breath cue, the side cue, and the pose. It doesn't matter if you use the same words over and over. Give them a good sequence, and stick with that sequence until you feel confident enough to experiment with vocabulary and incorporate new asanas.

4 **If you, like me,** constantly confuse your right and left limbs, wear bracelets and anklets. You will never find me teaching a class without a stack of malas on my left wrist.

5 **Take classes.** Once you've established yourself it is easy to fall into a rut. Taking classes gives you new ideas for sequencing and cueing. Don't worry about stealing ideas: we all do it, we all expect it, and if we were territorial about it, we wouldn't share it.

Seek and ye shall find

DON'T BE SHY: GO LOOKING FOR **OPPORTUNITIES** WHEREVER YOU ARE AND DON'T BE AFRAID TO CHARGE THE **RIGHT PRICE**

Even if you're just getting started in this game, there are still people out there who will want to work with you.

Inside, you may still feel a few insecurities, but if someone likes your teaching style and wants to hire you for private classes (where you'll earn much more than for regular classes), then take advantage of that opportunity. Many established teachers now only teach privates or one-to-ones.

There are other openings too for new yoga instructors, but they may not fall straight into your lap; it might require you to put in a bit of legwork.

Often, it's the go getters that get ahead, and for good reason too. Watch what's happening in your area, see who's doing what, and look for niche opportunities where you can.

COVERING CLASSES

This is bound to come up fairly on in your career as you commence paid teaching work. Covering a class at first brings on excitement at being given the opportunity to take over from an experienced, popular regular teacher. But it can also bring on an attack of nerves and angst if you start comparing your relative lack of experience.

Then there's the look of disappointment on student faces when they see their regular teacher hasn't shown up. Instead it's you: the sub. The feeling is a bit like being picked last for the team at sports in school.

But stick to your guns and stay true to yourself in the face of this pressure. You may be tempted to teach what you think the class want, instead of what feels instinctively right. That might breed further insecurity and to more 'I'm not good enough' feelings. You serve no one by comparing yourself to others.

It takes courage to stand up and share what you've learned with others, particularly as a new teacher. It also takes courage to be yourself rather than the best impression of your favourite teacher. So stay true to yourself. Teach what feels right in your heart. Be bold, cross your fingers, then jump in.

CORPORATE WORK

Corporate classes are great if you can get your hands on them. Teaching a captive audience inside a company (large or small) is a great way to start building your business.

Finding a way in is usually the hardest part (and I'm not talking about looking for the door). It's not easy to get into the big companies, but if you do, give them a taste of something sweet first to wake people up, a bit like a Trojan Horse. Get their attention.

This is an area where it pays to build connections with your local community. It's possible you may be asked to sub for another teacher, and you may even be approached, but it's more likely that you'll have to carve out these openings for yourself.

Here, it pays to be creative, to think of ways in which you can add value to an organisation (businesses, charities, public sector), and provide a cost effective solution to help them. Then it's about being in the right place at the right time. Remember: if you don't ask, you don't get.

PRIVATES/ONE-TO-ONES

These are a great way to boost your income and work more closely with your students. They're not just for the rich and famous: many are just beginners who want to learn a few basics before venturing into a class and put on a public display; others like the security and discretion that a private class offers.

They are great for yoga teachers as well, not only because they command a higher fee but they can be done in the comfort of your own home (if you have the space) or in the student's home.

Make it easy for students to tap into this service: that means make sure they know that you can offer this in the first place. Be as flexible as you can to allow them to have their yoga class when and where they want it.

Think safety too: both sides need to let someone know where they'll be and what time they're expected home. Arrange to send someone a quick text at the start and end of a session. When it comes to privates and one-to-ones, personal recommendation (for both student and teacher) is always the best way to start off.

What to charge

Privates command a much higher fee than a regular class. The solitary student gets your undivided attention for an hour or so, plus you may have to travel to get to them, which all costs time and money. As they're more intensive, the sessions can be more exhausting too, so make sure you charge an appropriate fee. If you're teaching celebrities the usual rules apply: charge what you like. But if it's the average man or woman on the street then you're looking at a fee that should reflect tuition time, travel time and cost, plus profit, and all pinned to your relevant level of experience. Private fees vary wildly. Charge more if you have to travel to the client. And don't be shy: it's got to be worth your while otherwise you'll not be able to keep it up. Look at what local studios are charging. If the studio charges £65 for an hour's one-to-one (and the teacher there will typically get about half of this, once fees and taxes have been deducted), then maybe you can fix a price that comes under this to be more competitive.

Kristin Ann Janishefski,
AGENCY DIRECTOR, THE VANGUARD PR

USE PR SKILLS TO ACCESS THE MEDIA
There are so many ways a PR specialist can help a yoga teacher. Our main goal is to promote the vision and philosophy of any specific teacher in a unique, relevant, and interesting way that appeals to their target consumer demographic.

WE HELP TO BUILD CREDIBILITY
A PR agency helps to establish credibility in their client's market, be it yoga or any other (we also work with eco, green and sustainable brands), through working with the media (locally, nationally, and internationally) to secure press placements.

THE RISE OF THE YOGA CELEBRITY
The use of PR is definitely a very common practice here in the US and Canada, as well as in Australia (where we also work). I definitely feel that, especially here in the US, there is a big craze right now for 'yoga celebrities'. We see many yogis who have agents, publicists and managers that handle their business while they focus on teaching and brand endorsement deals. I think it's so amazing to see this huge shift in consumer awareness for the yoga industry as a whole, which can be capitalised through PR.

WE GET MANY & VARIED YOGA REQUESTS
The requests we get from yoga personalities are mainly to increase brand awareness of their name, as well as of any products (such as books, DVDs) that they may be launching, through placement in the media. Also, helping them to manage endorsements and brand sponsorship opportunities has been a huge part of our business. In a way, we also act as a management company on behalf of our clients.

YOGA ROCKSTAR TIP #10

'MAKE YOURSELF KNOWN'

"If you don't know many
teachers, go to classes
and introduce yourself.
Established teachers
are always looking for
someone to cover
their class"

Kathleen Stavert | *Canada*

write your story

Get Inspired

TRUST YOURSELF AND ALLOW YOURSELF THE TIME TO GROW AS A NEW TEACHER

Yoga is everywhere in Australia
There are so many new forms of yoga emerging (for example stand-up paddleboard yoga and yoga barre). I live in the eastern suburbs of Sydney and there are now studios on every corner.

Confidence plays a huge part
I had to trust that I knew my stuff and that my students wanted to hear what I had to say. I had to discover my own teaching style. As I grew more confident it started to flow naturally.

Don't do too much too soon | As soon as I finished teacher training, I jumped straight in and took on eight or so classes a week, on top of my already busy schedule. This was too many, but I was excited to share what I'd learnt and, in a way, wanted to reassure myself

that I could teach. I've now stripped the classes back and have found better balance and space.

Do other work that's complementary | I only teach a few classes a week now so my other work is definitely necessary. I enjoy variety and am lucky enough to work within the health and wellness industry, writing about yoga and meditation. My teaching lends itself perfectly to my other work, and visa versa.

Just go for it | Immerse yourself in your own practice in every way possible. It's what you understand and discover within your body that is your greatest resource of information. It's a beautiful gift to give, and nothing beats an after-yoga class hug. It's pure bliss.

best advice:

Teaching from that authentic place within you is so important. Really letting that shine out, and remembering that you're only one person and you're human. You never know how much you can inspire someone, just by being yourself.

Kate Duncan AUSTRALIA

The boring stuff

NO ONE GOES INTO **YOGA** FOR THE **BOOKKEEPING.** ITS JUST ONE OF THOSE THINGS THAT'S GOT TO BE DONE

I n my fantasy world, life as a freelance writer is filled with trips to exotic destinations, scooping prestigious journalism awards, and Hollywood producers knocking on the door to snap up my debut screenplay for a seven figure sum.

I should imagine the fantasy life of a yoga teacher is not too dissimilar: lounging on a Hawaiian beach sipping cocktails after you've guided Madonna through a blissful sunset sequence; hearing reports on the news that your charity work in the Congo has helped end years of conflict and raised gross domestic product by a staggering 37%, transforming the lives of millions.

You get the picture. Unfortunately, the lawyers, accountants and tax administrators of this world don't seem to get it. These guys want you to fill in forms all day, have the right paperwork, and generally steal away your dreams.

But they mean well. Actually, when you think about it, they're team players when it comes to getting your yoga business off the ground, and helping it stay afloat.

As dull as it sounds - and it is extremely dull - it's hard to overstate the importance of this side of the industry. Make sure your yoga business adds up when it comes to money, otherwise you won't have a yoga business for long.

That means paying close attention to your record keeping, tax affairs, insurance and any legal obligations.

No, you're not in this game for the money, or the pleasure of filing an annual tax return, but if you don't take it all seriously from the start then your yoga business is not going anywhere.

It may well be that you are the most charismatic, inspiring teacher to hit these shores in a decade, but if you can't pay the bills each month you'll soon be denied the opportunity to share that special gift. All it takes is a bit of time, so don't slack on the books.

I ♥ numbers

KEEP ON TOP OF YOUR **PAPERWORK** BEFORE IT PILES UP AND SWAMPS YOU

The best approach is to get your house in order before you begin. You don't need to understand all of the complexities of the tax system (no one does) or the seemingly inane insurance jargon, but you do need to make sure your basic systems are in place so things don't get out of hand as you grow.

This means getting insured - an insurance advisor will help you, but also talk to other teachers - and keeping your books up-to-date, right from the beginning.

Keep it simple so that you understand your own records and you know what's going on. If it stretches your brain too much, that's the time to ask for help.

If you keep good accounting records then it makes all the other things, like filing tax returns, that much simpler. There are plenty of software packages available to help you manage your affairs smoothly, whether you're a sole trader or running a string of studios.

Starting out, you may not need any of this, just be sure to keep it current and up-to-date. Yes, it's dull, but it has to be done.

Again, when things get complicated, just bring in the advice of an expert. It can take time to set things up properly at the beginning but it will be worth it in the end. The more attention you pay to this at the start, the better chance you'll have of making a career doing what you love.

Business basics

GET YOUR **GAME** FACE ON:
SIMPLE WAYS TO **ELEVATE** YOUR BUSINESS

IT'S A BUSINESS. If you want to make teaching yoga your full or part time career then you need to treat it like any other business: keep your basic accounts up-to-date daily, respond to enquires in a timely manner and always be professional when teaching.

CHOOSE YOUR NICHE within yoga and become an expert in your chosen field, whether that's yoga therapy, children's yoga, or yoga for sports. Whatever it is, become as knowledgeable in that field as possible. Your yoga teacher training certificate is only the very beginning of a long journey.

FREE PLACES. Unless it's for a charity or a specific cause, don't run free classes. The best way to make sure the right people get these is to award free 'karma places' to students who really need them. If you teach classes for free all the time you may end up feeling resentful (because you need money to pay your bills too) and low on *prana* (energy). If you do not allow students to pay you - be it donating or a set fee - there will be an imbalance in the exchange of energy.

give love

Understanding insurance

MAKE SURE YOU'VE GOT THE APPROPRIATE **COVER** FOR WHAT YOU ARE DOING BEFORE YOU START TAKING ANY **CLASSES**

Please get yourself properly insured. I know top international yoga instructors (no names!) who've worked uninsured, because of the cost involved. But they were lucky. It's never a good idea and potentially exposes you to financial and vocational ruin.

Try to view it all in a positive light. It's genuinely a good thing. Insurance can be the difference between losing your livelihood or not; it's also vital for promoting a professional image to the world and to protect the public at large.

Moreover, in today's claims culture, aided by the rise of 'no win, no fee' lawyers, the ability to sue is no longer restricted to the rich and famous, so cover your ass before it's too late.

Get protected

The right cover will vary according to where you are but may include public liability, medical malpractice, breach of confidentiality, financial loss, criminal and tax defence, loss of reputation and products liability. There are many other types of protection too: to cover contents, buildings, items taken away from premises such as mobile equipment and laptops, loss of profits arising from damage to your premises, protecting yourself or colleagues for loss of income due to illness, accident or death and so on. For corporate entities with multi therapist clinics, businesses selling health products or other commercial ventures, there are various special packages available too.

Moving forward

DON'T GET STUCK IN A RUT WHEN YOU'RE JUST STARTING OUT. SEE THE **WORLD** WITH **FRESH** EYES

I f all this talk of insurance is getting you down then it's time for some more yoga. Yes, these are things you need to think about, so get them done, but then move on to more interesting stuff.

Look for creative ways to move your business forward. Set yourself up for success.

That could mean hanging on to your other job for now. Doing what you want to do full time, but on a part time basis, creates a cushion; it's the same with any new business.

Set your minimum earning targets and then go about generating multiple sources of income (including any non-yoga work): public classes, gyms, privates, corporates. Use all of these to build up the minimum teaching hours (and income) to support yourself.

An average might be 15-20 classes per week to pay the rent but it really depends on where you live and your lifestyle; and that would be a lot of classes for a new teacher to cope with.

There will always be naysayers, those that say 'you'll never make it', or 'you'll end up back in the corporate world'. But do you know what? Just prove 'em wrong. So many others before you already have.

Yoga is needed everywhere so you can teach almost anywhere. Get creative in how you approach this. Go into non-traditional environments, put your foot in the door. Carry your business wherever you go and be ready to answer questions and make suggestions.

HERE ARE A FEW OTHER TIPS:

Book appointments with people as face-to-face contact is always better. Don't just show up on the door, do it professionally.

Work on your 'audition'. Preparation leads to opportunity, so barter with a confidence coach or a life coach for lessons if you're unsure of yourself. Have a thick skin for all the rejections you'll get. Persistence pays off.

Help gyms set up a yoga programme. The classes might grow, students might ask for privates; people will start to seek out your services if you are good.

The more people you can reach though your public classes (in gyms, or studios, or wherever), the more people you can eventually funnel through to more lucrative work later on (when you start hosting retreats and workshops).

Some people may be willing to go to a community centre because it's not scary (whereas a yoga studio can be a scary place for newbies). So start a community centre yoga class. Maybe the students will follow you to a yoga studio later on as they get comfortable.

Burn out

TAKE **GOOD** CARE OF YOURSELF WHILE YOU'RE TAKING CARE OF **BUSINESS**

Teaching can sometimes feel quite isolating, trekking around from one place to the next, not really having any colleagues. Yes, you create this connection with your students for an hour or so but then you're off to the next class. It can feel lonely at times.

Be mindful of this (although there's no better way to learn to love yourself and accept your shortcomings than to become a yoga teacher).

Stepping into this role requires a great deal of presence and compassion. You're being introduced to so many bodies and minds that you begin to see how deeply vulnerable humans can be but equally how radiant they all are.

All this activity, however (chasing about for work, moving from one studio to the next), can leave you fragmented and frazzled in these early days. You're taking on classes right now that might not be rewarding for you later on.

In time, you can start to put some roots down but for now be careful not to get burnt out. Yes, you do have to make some sacrifices, so try and compensate with simple lifestyle changes. Take a day out, spend time in nature to recharge, thrive on the energy of your students, be sure to find time to nourish yourself.

If you end up teaching so much that you lose your self-practice, or even your love of yoga, then its time to stop and rethink or adjust your schedule.

Remember you are here to build and then sustain a long-term career. It's not about the quantity of your classes, it's about the quality of your classes.

And quality will always win through in the end.

A word on ethics

Oh, and a word on ethics too (not that you need it, of course, being of pure mind and spirit). Etiquette states that you don't market your classes for one venue when you're inside working in another; take that conversation outside. You can can do it, but it's not the nicest thing to do. But you know that already right? And when it comes to managing student/teacher relationships, tread with extreme caution as this is a minefield; talk to your studio boss, or other teachers before you dive in. If in doubt, don't go there.

How I made it happen

BUDOKON CREATOR SAYS STICK TO YOUR GUNS AND NEVER COMPROMISE

Cameron Shayne USA

Be your best ambassador | Build your reputation on solid ground. Keep your word and agreements. Be kind, and treat everyone as an equal. Stay hungry and patient. The journey is the point. A foolish mind does something thinking of being finished with it. There is no learning in that mind state. Be authentic and honest. Don't 'people please'. Be best of brand in every way. Don't settle for 'almost' or 'close enough'.

Determination certainly trumps talent | The intention and discipline to continue forward, until a level of skill is reached, can be a far greater asset than raw talent. We're talking about long-term staying power. There's a difference between the modern yoga teachers that gain awareness via social media, versus the teacher that teaches and tours, and stays the course for many years. These teachers form long-lasting relationships with long-term students. See your career as a life-long journey.

Learn to take the rough with the smooth | Establishing Budokon was, in ways, effortless, and in other ways, painfully slow. I was never able to sacrifice the quality of the art form for profit. This is something any young creator experiences. There are massive temptations to compromise in exchange for comfort. I would, to this day, rather be less financially successful than have the reputation of a capitalist. I teach because I love it; it's my work. Pure and simple.

Stay awake through the journey | When times are tough, I pay attention to the thoughts I'm having, and from where they originate. I don't judge them or try to correct them. I just let them come and go, staying curious. Conclusions are for people addicted to suffering; I am not that man. Freedom comes from non-attachment.

let's roll

best advice:

Teach from your personal experience. Not from what you read, or believe to be true. All personal beliefs are traps. They change like the wind. Avoid them. Focus on learning, studying, studentship. Teaching is nothing but an advanced learning process.

6

M is for marketing

"None but ourselves can free our mind"

Bob Marley

surrender and release

Leave a little sparkle wherever you go

What's all this marketing stuff about?

GET YOUR **MIND** AROUND MARKETING TO SEE YOUR BUSINESS **SOAR**

Now, we're getting to the good stuff. Yep, marketing.

Together with passion, determination, confidence and resilience, this is something you'll need to master at some point.

You don't have to do any marketing at all if you don't want to – but your chances of making a long and profitable career will be virtually zero.

Play the marketing game well, though, and there's no reason why your business can't thrive.

Here's the simple truth about marketing: if no one knows about you, or what you do, then how can they buy your product?

It's the same for any business: whether you're running your first yoga class, or opening a big studio, or even a local pet store, marketing is pretty darn essential.

Yes folks, this 'M' word really matters. If there's one extra set of skills you need to acquire to make it as a successful and commercial yoga instructor then this is it. So listen up.

Luckily, you don't need a degree in marketing or to hire an expert to get your student numbers up or to start building your own following.

You just need to be your own beautiful, authentic self, get creative, and roll your sleeves up for some real work. Lets get going!

Reality bites

BE **PREPARED** FOR A **REALITY** CHECK.
STARTING WITH THAT FIRST CLASS

No one said this yoga journey was going to be easy.

In fact, your reality check will probably come quite soon after you graduate and actually start paid teaching work.

Although friends and family might come along to support you on your opening night, your chances of survival long-term rest on getting new people - total strangers, in fact - interested enough to check you out and, ultimately, step through the door and hand over their hard earned cash for your classes.

A daunting prospect for some, but no different or greater a challenge than any other business owner faces.

All it means is successfully promoting yourself - your studio, your retreats, or your new eco friendly clothing range, whatever it is you're selling - to your potential customers.

And that means (yep, you guessed it) marketing.

Memorise this, guys: marketing (or promotion or PR, or whatever you want to call it) is absolutely essential if you want a thriving and successful yoga career.

There ain't no shortcuts.

The marketing matrix

THE NUMBER OF **PROMOTIONAL TRICKS** AT YOUR DISPOSAL IS VIRTUALLY **LIMITLESS**

Traditional marketing is alive and well, you'll be pleased to hear. You don't have to be a Facebook fiend (although it helps) to get students through the doors, there are plenty of other tools in the toolkit to get a successful yoga business up and running.

They include:
Flyers
Business cards
Special offers
Word of mouth
Referrals and partners
Getting out and about
Media coverage

Online marketing you may have noticed, however, that there has been a digital revolution in the last 20 years or so. As well as TV sets in the home, most folks now have (at least) one computer plus portable tablets and smart phones. These things now compete for our attention in the sitting rooms of millions of homes the world over. There's a long list of digital marketing solutions and possibilities now at your fingertips, right this second.

They include:
Websites
Databases
Email newsletters
Mobile phones
Social media

Help yourself

ANYONE CAN DO THEIR OWN **MARKETING.** IT JUST TAKES A LITTLE **THOUGHT** FIRST

The good news is marketing is much easier than it sounds. There's no need for any cold calling (you're not selling double glazing, after all), so you'll need no special sales training, and you certainly don't need a degree from Harvard.

All you need to do is just get your earnest yoga message out there, explaining precisely what you do and how you can help people.

After all, your job is not selling yoga classes, is it? No, you're in the business of helping others transform and better their lives. Yoga classes are just the means to pay for this important and noble purpose.

Okay, we get it! Now, tell us how to promote ourselves. Here, the world's your oyster. You are only limited, in fact, by your imagination.

Marketing can be obvious, like taking out paid advertising in a local newspaper, or sticking business cards and posters in shop windows. Some of this 'old school' stuff can cost you money, however.

If you're clever, you may be able to drum up press interest (more on this later). Getting people together to raise money for charity is always a great way to get the press on your side.

But generating interest in your business can be done in far more subtle

Brutal truths

What they tell you, quite brutally, when first starting out in travel journalism is that 'no one cares about your holiday'. Assume then that 'no one cares about your classes' either. From that lowly, worst-case, starting point, you need to entice clients in with the promise of something special. What you're offering is perfectly valid; you just need to say it and present it the right way. In writing, there are so many different ways to say the same thing; the same can be said for promoting a yoga class. Just give it some thought before you engage with your audience to make your classes a 'must-have'.

have no regrets

ways too, for example, community building via online social media. This is a huge and (mostly) free opportunity, and it's not just for the younger generation either; we're all at it these days. Many of the world's top yoga teachers and brands are masters of this domain, and it's only set to grow in the future.

Though not all follow this path; it's got to feel right for you.

Meet their needs

What you're after in all cases (whatever marketing approach you take) is to get your unique message across: what it is you're offering people and, more importantly, how it can help them in their day-to-day lives.

The trick is in how you present that message.

Here's an example: strangers don't care if you're offering a 7pm beginner's Hatha class at the church hall on Tuesday nights. You might get lucky, but you might not.

However, people may respond better if you can tap into a specific need of theirs: your class could be targeting office workers on their way home, promising them an hour of stress relief or back care after sitting at their desk all day.

Or it could be aimed at helping mums grab some much-needed quiet time after a full day with the kids.

They're buying into your classes (and ultimately, you) for how it makes them feel, and for what they stand to gain, not just because you're making the effort to host them.

It's a subtle difference but an important one.

Students want you

The challenge initially is simply getting people to give you a try. Once they do - and if they like what they see and hear in your class - then they'll come back for more.

Marketing at this stage just means letting people know that you're around, and going about it in a way that will focus on or address their issues and needs. They want to get something out of their class; they're not just there to support you, or to see that the hall isn't empty that night.

If you can convince them to walk through the door then you've done very well. After that, it's a case of letting your extraordinary and beautiful self do the talking.

"You're in the business of helping others transform and better their lives. Yoga classes are just the means to pay for this"

YOGA ROCKSTAR TIP #11

'MAKE YOURSELF KNOWN'

"Use social media in a
clever way and try to
participate in as many
yoga conferences and
events as possible,
especially at the start, to
make yourself known"

Maya Fiennes | Macedonia

just do it

How much do I spend?

MARKETING DOESN'T HAVE TO COST THE EARTH

One big question you may have is how much this is all going to cost.

The good news is it doesn't have to cost a fortune. In fact, it can be virtually free if that's the way you choose to go.

It's wise in the beginning (and always, for that matter) to put a very strict budget on how much you're willing and able to spend, including on the basics like leaflets, flyers and business cards.

These are all great to have - and very important long-term, as they work for lots of people - but right from the start, you can skip it all if money is super tight.

Always save where you can: it's now possible to get business cards printed for free online. Make sure you check it out.

And be sure to maximise all available 'free' publicity outlets before you even contemplate spending anything. That means let everyone know what you're up to as you start your new yoga enterprise; don't be shy. Build a contact database and send out a regular email bulletin to keep your community (no matter how small at this stage) informed.

Online marketing can be extremely valuable in this regard.

Even if you can't afford (or don't want) your own website, social media is an opportunity not to be missed for the budget conscious.

Post regularly (but don't overdo it) on Facebook and other sites to let folks know what's going on. Try and be interesting when engaging with your audience. Make yourself available when people want further information. Be professional and respond promptly and courteously.

If you're gunning for press coverage, then the editorial team at the local newspaper are always on the lookout for good new stories. That's a great free resource if you can access it. It may not be easy at the start but there are some things you can do to tip the balance in your favour. Again, more on dealing with the press later.

Here's the most important thing to remember at this stage: get a strict marketing budget (even if that's a big fat zero) and stick to it. There are always 'unmissable opportunities' out there to part you with your money: advertising execs at newspapers and magazines will lure you in promising the world. It's all too easy to get carried away. Just don't go there. Identify your budget (even if that's zero) and never, ever break it. Ah, if only life were that easy!

Get creative

THERE ARE **NO LIMITS** WHEN IT COMES TO MARKETING. JUST STICK CLOSE TO YOUR CORE **PRINCIPLES**

I t's not rocket science. In fact, it's not science at all. It's more about being creative, and that's something that comes naturally to a lot of yogis.

Watch what other successful teachers do: ask the people you admire or those that you trained with and see what works for them. Just mirror them for a while until you gain more confidence.

Check out what others are doing too in terms of marketing to see what works and what looks good. Use that as a starting point.

Then simply sprinkle on your own unique and incredible magical marketing dust and watch your yoga business fly.

C OME FROM THE HEART
If all this is starting to make you feel uncomfortable, then take heart: at the end of the day, all you're really doing is offering a heartfelt service that you think will be of tremendous value to others. That's the most important thing to hold on to.

All this marketing stuff is about is you getting that genuine message out to others in order to help them.

So, do what you're doing with authenticity and you can't go too far wrong, whatever form of marketing you start dabbling in.

You want to help people to live better lives. The marketing bit is just letting them know that. Respond to their needs, offer what the customer wants, but always do it from a place of sincerity.

B ELIEVE IN YOURSELF
No matter how big you get it's a nice idea to always keep some donation-based or free yoga classes running every so often as a 'give back' to your community and the less advantaged people out there.

It shows you've got a big heart. And people will always respond to that.

It can be a challenge perhaps to maintain that level of authenticity with a new consumer group that is fast evolving in an electronic world but that's a challenge that we all face. Believe in what you do, get that honesty out there, and your students will respond for sure.

Let your authenticity direct your marketing.

dazzle them

Get Inspired

CAROLE MORITZ SUPPLEMENTS HER TEACHING WITH WRITING AND OTHER CREATIVE WORK

Age shouldn't be a barrier | As a mature instructor, I wasn't sure there'd be a place for me beyond church halls. But opportunities keep presenting themselves that motivate me to keep moving forward.

Make it your own | Yoga adapts itself to the era, which is why it has lasted all these thousands of years. Perhaps your yoga isn't even on the mat; perhaps you find it on a basketball court. For others, it's wearing a cute yoga top with a brightly coloured mat, or just sipping an organic green juice. It's all good.

Yoga is now a global business | With yoga becoming more a part of the mainstream, it makes it more accessible. Yoga's not a threat to any religion, moral or political stance, and is now finding its way into classrooms, offices and military bases; it's also recognised as a viable option for stress management.

Don't go into it for the money Yoga isn't necessarily a business entered into as a primary income. We do it because we love it. Usually there needs to be another income stream, and because teaching is physically demanding you have to be honest about the quantity of classes to teach.

Rewards come in other ways | Many of us will never recoup our investment in training and continuing education, but that shouldn't discourage anyone from pursuing a teaching career. Like anything that doesn't generate sustainable income, you must still take care of yourself, regardless, and be responsible to those depending on you.

Writing is a good back-up The only way you can write about yoga is to sit butt in chair and write, write, write. After that, write some more. Do your research. Scour websites, go to newsstands and look at magazines.

best advice:

Starting out, I tormented myself: my Midwestern work ethic argued that yoga wasn't a 'real' job and that I needed to stop fooling around. I say stop the self-flagellation that's going on and get to work making yoga your 'real' job.

Carole Moritz USA

Traditional marketing tools

FAMILIARISE YOURSELF WITH THESE 'OLD SCHOOL' MARKETING METHODS AND YOU'RE HALF WAY THERE

BUSINESS CARDS
They may be small, but business cards form an integral part of your sales pitch. That may sound a bit corporate but this is a competitive world; if you want the gig, then you've got to go for it. Business cards can be one-sided or double-sided, colour or black & white. Make them stand out but be tasteful and succinct too. Oh, and do get someone to check over your spelling, just in case. You can get these done for free if you search around a bit online. They certainly don't have to be expensive; if they are, then go to another supplier.

WORD OF MOUTH
This is like marketing gold dust. If you're offering a fabulous service then sooner or later people will start talking about it. And yoga students do talk to each other a lot. This is a great way to get more of them - and it requires little additional input from you - but it's hard to control, of course. All you can do is be the best that you can be and let karmic forces work their unpredictable magic. A word of caution: this works both ways. If you're not pleasing your students then they may well go away and talk about that too. Give them your fabulous self each and every day, just to be on the safe side. I love this saying: when you treat your customers with respect, they will do your marketing for free.

FLYERS
There's an art to designing good flyers. Get a friend to help if this is tricky for you, or if you struggle with computers. Flyers are great for many things. Find out more about these marvelous creations in the next chapter (on promoting your workshops and retreats).

SPECIAL OFFERS
A great way to get more students and it doesn't have to cost you a dime. Introductory offers (such as unlimited classes, or an 'All the yoga you can eat' monthly pass) are appealing and can help get new people through the doors. Follow-up offers for existing students are also good for retaining business (for instance, offering 10 classes for the price of nine, or even a discounted tariff if you sign up within a set month,

eat for energy

or before a subscription expires). At the very least make sure the first class is free. It doesn't cost you anything; it just provides a little incentive to get people to check you out without making any big commitment. And that's all you want.

REFERRALS AND PARTNERS

All good businesses do this, hooking up with other local firms and organisations to offer special deals. So, maybe pair up with strategic partners like a local massage therapist to offer yoga classes with a discount if they send customers your way. In return, you do the same. There's almost unlimited scope so get to know your local business community to see how you can work together. If you're brave enough, you may even want to work with other yoga teachers to market each others classes. What? Won't they'll steal my students?

Maybe they will, maybe they won't. But if you're offering a Thursday night class when no one else is then it might be good to let other teachers know that; in return, you'll flag up their Tuesday night session. Almost always, cooperation is a better way to do business.

GETTING OUT AND ABOUT

This is more time-intensive but it can be fun if you're creative with it. Yoga flash mobs - taking to the streets for some pop-up yoga sessions - have become all the rage these days. It's a good way of getting out there and getting seen. And if you have a special message, like a charitable venture to promote, then all the better. Collect money as you go and promote your

business in the process. Win-win. This can be fun too: recruit strangers off the street, show them a good time. Host your impromptu class in front of one of your city's most famous or quirky landmarks. That's a photo oppurtunity.

LOCAL PRESS

The journalists at your local newspaper are worth befriending. They're busy people so make it easy for them, and don't throw a strop if they reject your ideas. If you're patient, and offer story angles that are of real interest to them, then they'll warm to you very quickly (they're a shallow bunch; I know because I'm one of them). Think up inventive story possibilities - like taking a mini yoga session outside the town hall for council staff (pop-up yoga), and see if they'll send a photographer along. Throw in a charity message and you can't go wrong. If all else fails, offer to go into the newspaper offices to offer some simple desk-based stretching for free. They'll appreciate the stress relief, and you'll get to hang out with them and get to know them. Just don't do it on press day or they'll bite your head off. It takes time to nurture these relationships but it can be worth it in the long-run. Read more on the media and dealing with the press in chapter 10.

PUBLIC RELATIONS

Hiring a PR expert can be a fantastic way to get results but it can be expensive. Monthly retainers can range anywhere from $1,000-$5,000. Fine if you're at the top of your game, but tricky for newcomers.

> *"when you treat your customers with respect, they will do your marketing for free"*

Go digital, baby

PLUG IN AND PLAY: MAKE THE VIRTUAL **WORLD WORK** FOR YOUR BUSINESS

As well as 'old school' marketing tricks you now have at your disposal a vast array of digital and electronic lines of communication with your potential clients. The sooner you embrace this technology, the better. Don't be afraid of it. If you are, then go on a course, it'll make your business life much easier. None of this is mandatory, but the more you do, the better chance you'll have of reaching your community.

Follow these simple digital marketing tips to get your cyber calling card out there in a flash.

1 Build a website. Even if it's just a simple 'calling card' site with contact details there must be an online space where students can locate you. A great website - one that looks good, is easy to navigate, and highlights your irresistible offer - is even better.

2 Use keywords. Be sure to use the right 'keywords' on your site so it's easy to find when prospective students search for you on google. Think creatively with possible search terms so that you can easily be picked up by search engines. More on this later.

3 Collect email addresses. Don't be afraid to add new email addresses to your computer database and provide regular mailings. This may not sit right with some, so make sure there is an easy 'unsubscribe' option. If you do it right, though, this can be a great way of keeping in touch with your student community on the cheap.

4 Add value. Make your email bulletins (and all marketing blurb) readable and engaging. Include useful information such as advice on a posture or sequence, a simple meditation, or a positive affirmation or quote, even a nice picture. Your students will love you for it. It's so much better than just blurting out how much your class costs.

5 Start a Facebook page. Once you're comfortable online, social media is the next step forward. Hang out where your students hang out. Look for their FB pages and befriend them. Great for building relationships and communities. Keep them up-to-date with posts and try to make them fun and interesting.

6 Get graphic. Visuals are perfect to grab interest. So, next time you're in the park, take that photo of you in that incredible asana and post it. A picture with a short caption is a very effective way to standout online.

be content

Great websites

YOU DON'T HAVE TO BE A **NERD** TO BE AN ONLINE YOGA **SUCCESS**

What makes a website great? I can imagine web masters from all over the world arguing all weekend long over this one at some techie conference in Vegas. Leave them to their nerdy ways. That doesn't really concern us here.

All you need to know are the basics. You can build websites yourself these days thanks to the wonders of user-friendly interface technology but if you can find a developer to do it for you it'll look so much better.

This is your shop window to the world so you want to make it beautiful and appealing to entice people inside. Don't expect miracles: they're not going to book a year's worth of classes because you've got nice photos on there. They may, however, email or call you, which is all you're after at this stage.

Write content (or get someone to write it) that describes exactly what it is you're offering. Take your time on this. Try and make it inspiring, but don't be too flowery. Simple is always best. Convey what you need to convey as briefly as possible, it makes for more compelling reading.

And you'll need to deploy 'keywords' in there to make it easier for people to find you as well when they search for yoga in your area. These are simple phrases such as 'Yoga for children' or 'Yoga in Plymouth'. Sometimes these can seem a bit contrived and detract from your sparkling prose but they're very important nonetheless. If no one can find you out there on google and the big worldwide web then why bother?

Other things to think about:
Include contact details. Make sure there's a phone number people can reach you on and, of course, an email address. If you can give out a physical location - easy if you have a studio - that's great, but you really don't want people turning up on your doorstep, so no home addresses please.

Do include 'link' buttons (or 'badges') for people to follow straight through to your Facebook page (or social media). Digital savvy teachers have a whole string of these badges for each social media channel permanently displayed on their site. It's a means of keeping the traffic flowing within your community.

Keep your site up-to-date. There's nothing more depressing than a website that hasn't been touched or looked at for years. It makes me feel sad. So, post regular news items or anything that takes your fancy, that you think will engage your community. Keep it fresh.

YOGA ROCKSTAR TIP #12

'TAKE YOUR TIME'

"Take your time. Nothing will make or break your career, so if something slips through your hands, just keep moving on"

Kathryn Budig | USA

go for it

Starting out in social media

IT'S NEVER TOO LATE TO **HARNESS** THOSE **SOCIAL** MEDIA **SKILLS**

Gulp! I dont do any of that social media stuff!
    If that sounds like you then read on...

If you're already into social media - perhaps you're a yoga Instagrammer posting selfies every single day, or you're never off Facebook - then just skip to the next chapter.

But if you're not even sure what a 'tweet' is then stay tuned.

The best advice in this case is to head to a social media course if you can, or at least ask some pals what it's all about. That should be enough to get you started. The rest is experimentation and, yes, even having fun with it.

This area can be mind-boggling for newcomers, but don't let that put you off. You don't have to master them all. Many yoga teachers just use one or two social media sites very successfully (although there are many that still don't use any).

Find one or two that you enjoy doing and stick with those ones. If you start using one social media platform that just doesn't feel right, then don't use it, find another.

If you're more into the visual side of things then Instagram might work for you. This has been extremely popular with countless yoga teachers around the world keen to show off their physical prowess.

A number of teachers have made their names from doing this, generating a huge following along the way. Top Instagrammers carry real clout.

If you like writing then you might enjoy Twitter, posting updates throughout the day to your students who want to know about the green juice you had for breakfast or the theme for tonight's class.

If you're scared of it all still, just sign up and have a little nose around to see what it's all about before posting anything.

THE BIG ONES

**Twitter / Facebook
Google + / Pinterest
Youtube / Linkedin
Instagram / Tumblr**
And probably many
more coming soon...

What's the point?

IF YOU'RE **NEW** TO ALL THIS **STUFF,** YOU MAY RIGHTLY ASK WHAT'S THE POINT OF **SOCIAL MEDIA?**

Surely yoga is all about getting away from this techie stuff to enjoy our connection with each other, and the natural world around us?

Yes, that's true, but here's the point: people don't like being sold to. They're not dummies. Social media is all about relationship marketing, building that all-important community that yoga's foundations depend on. It just happens to be online. You're effectively building a community here, in part, so that you don't have to sell directly.

It's fun, friendly and can be very worthwhile from a business perspective (albeit in a non- traditional 'selling' way).

And it's not a sprint; it's more of a long race.

If the thought of diving into all those social media platforms is bewildering (and there'll probably be more of them along soon as the next generation of Silicon Valley hotshots looks to make another fast billion) then start out with Facebook. This flagship site still drives masses more internet traffic then any of the others (probably all of the others combined), and it's still growing.

Interestingly, the fastest growing age group now signing up to FB are the so-called Silver Surfers (mature folks) who are using it to stay in touch with the grandchildren in Australia, or for online shopping.

Yes, Instagram, Pinterest and Snapchat are all groovy, and very popular with the younger set, but it's still (for now) FB that's the big hitter. Twitter (one that I enjoy personally) drives a fraction of the internet traffic that FB does.

So perhaps start there and use that as your hub as you explore others.

Time vacuum

A common social media criticism is that it can be a time vacuum. So be disciplined about this. There's no point doing any of it if it's not going to bolster your business, of course. Make sure you keep the long-term picture (growing your community, spreading your brand) in mind. Have fun doing it, though. That's important too.

Get Inspired

ANN-MARGARET GRAHAM, A FULL-TIME WORKING MUM IN NOVA SCOTIA, SEES HER YOGA TEACHING AS A WHOLE NEW ADVENTURE IN LIFE

Be prepared for self-doubt | From teacher training to getting my feet wet as an instructor was nothing like I expected. I questioned the money I was investing, the strain on my relationships, the energy it took emotionally, and whether I had what it took to lead a class. I'm not sure anyone could have warned me about it.

I knew that I wanted to teach | Through this journey I discovered that I not only wanted to teach, but that I loved to teach. The idea that I have been given the opportunity to share what I have felt so much passion for is an honour and a blessing.

Starting anything new can be daunting | The main challenges we all face are probably those that we impose against ourselves. Transitioning from the role of student to that of a teacher can bring up plenty of fear and self-doubt.

Emotions were high before my first class | I felt shy and unsure, and small, somehow, like I hadn't grown enough, that I still had so much to learn. Through all that uncertainty and vulnerability, I was still able to find a childlike excitement. Here I was, at 44, starting something new, which felt absolutely fantastic.

Teaching can be a thrill | My biggest thrill came six weeks into teaching my first group. I brought them all into Warrior 2, giving the usual cues they'd become familiar with. When I looked at them, I felt my heart swell with pride. I couldn't believe how amazing they were, it almost brought me to tears. I felt like a proud mother.

best advice:

I've found it helpful to remind myself that it's okay to mess up and that I'm still growing. I've defined and connected to my reasons for wanting to teach, and I always come back to that in times of doubt.

Ann-Margaret Graham CANADA

Making friends with Facebook

BUILD YOUR COMMUNITY ONLINE

UNDERSTAND YOUR TARGET MARKET BEFORE YOU GET GOING: How old are they? What are their interests? Where do they spend their time online? Why would they use your services?

KNOW WHAT MESSAGES WILL RESONATE WITH YOUR AUDIENCE: This will help you create the kind of content that will appeal, whether that's fun photos, poems, yoga sequences or interesting news articles. What you're after is to get people to 'Like' or 'Share' your content (the phraseology varies depending on

Business Pages

Do set up a Business page or Public page on FB (even if it unsettles your ego doing so, or the fact that you might have to call yourself a 'public figure'). It's fine to have both a Public page and a regular FB page (for friends and family). Make sure when you configure it that anyone and everyone can view it. This is not the time to be shy. And it's a good idea to add someone else as an administrator too (a friend, relative or trusted colleague) just in case you get locked out. It happens. Use a good header photo of yourself, your logo, or something that shows off your business in an instant, and make sure that you keep any blurb punchy, succinct and relevant.

what platform you're on), or enter into a dialogue with you. This all helps build connection and community.

HOW OFTEN TO POST: social media experts differ on this. On FB, some say seven posts a week, one per day; others say just three posts a week is enough. Of course, you'll also need to engage with those people that respond to you, so it all takes time. Manage your time effectively.

Scheduling: FB allows you to load up your posts for the week ahead through a scheduling service. It means you don't have to be on the site every day even if you are posting every day. It's a useful tool altough you still need to monitor traffic and reply if necessary. Another service, Hootsuite, allows you to post to multiple platforms.

WHAT TO POST: anything that'll engage, entertain or educate your audience: images, quotes, links, infographics (information in image form). As a general rule, people love images and are less likely to read text updates (especially long ones), so don't waste time writing a mini essay.

STATUS UPDATES: people only tend to read one sentence. You don't need to write War and Peace. Save that for your website, where people can go if they really want to see what you're about.

WHAT ABOUT ME: post direct business details (workshops, classes, retreats) sparingly. This means your 'direct selling' gets diluted by all the fun stuff, so you're not a tiresome online bore (which will make people disengage quicker than you can say *Trikonasana*).

HOW DO I GET 'LIKES': On FB Business or Public pages you get 'likes' rather than collect 'friends'. It takes time to build the numbers up but there are things that you can do (including paying for the privilege). Invite your friends first, then import your contacts (use any email addresses you've been collecting), and then find any other yoga teachers you like, see who's following them, then simply follow them. Easy. And the same goes for any other relevant groups too, such as yoga clothing firms, or the trade media (follow individual journalists too, as well as the newspapers or magazines themselves). You can pay to promote your page too with FBs online tools.

FACEBOOK INSIGHTS: Once you've got 30 'likes' you'll have access to Facebook Insights. These are analytical tools which you can use to monitor traffic and peak times. Eventually, this will help you work out when to upload your content for maximum effect.

STAY ENGAGING: never say "please like or share my post"; it's so boring. And if you only talk about your work you become a work bore. Offer a little extra value, some bits of fun, and don't insult people's intelligence. Just be yourself.

Other things to think about:

THE RIGHT TIME: find the best time of day to post status updates. A large number of posts never even get seen. Insights will help you with this.

AFFINITY: the more people like/click your posts, the more they will tend to see.

STORY BUMPS: basically re-telling old posts. So, if someone comments on one of your posts you want to comment back, which will help keep it at the top of the feed. You can keep stories high up the order for around 10 days this way.

ASK QUESTIONS: force people to react (or click or like). How are people feeling? Do they prefer A or B? Even if someone just says 'I like your page' always reply to say 'thank you' to keep things alive and engaged. It's dull but all part of the game.

REMEMBER, PEOPLE ARE NOSEY: they'll see all your interaction and be inclined to check it out. Always look to build that conversation, that's where your community-building happens.

VIDEO CONTENT: short video is great if you can do it. Post on YouTube first and then put it on FB, so it transfers across all devices smoothly. (That's provided the video is of good quality. Don't post garbage on there. More on this later).

EVENTS & MILESTONES: to generate interest you can add one of these, like a countdown to a retreat or workshop or maybe a one hour online Q&A session with you to discuss a specific issue (back pain, stress). The reality is people can post anytime they like but it creates a little extra buzz. It also gets them talking which is what you want.

FACEBOOK ADS: these are highly effective. You can do them by location and industry, and are reasonably cheap.

Meet the gang

THE **BEST** WAY TO **UNDERSTAND** ALL OF THE SOCIAL MEDIA PLATFORMS IS TO **EXPLORE** THEM FIRST HAND

FACEBOOK: You can start your profile building for free here even if you don't yet have a website. FB is almost synonymous with social media now. It's still hugely popular and for good reason, allowing you to reach out to like-minded souls locally and the world over. The downside is that the evil FB masterminds are now charging to promote your posts. In the good old days, everything was free. Over time, this could promote a migration to other platforms, although for now, this is probably the main one to get started on. Use this as your hub.

INSTAGRAM: This has become mega fashionable among the yoga set, and is basically a depository of imagery for the beautiful, athletic elite. As a rule, this is more of a young person's thing but that's likely to change as more mature folks discover it. It's incredibly simple to use and the in-built tools allow you to polish up your photos too. Some yogis have gone on to build enormous followings via their Instagram accounts. Check them out: there are some amazing sights on there that will dazzle you and inspire you. If you're great at yoga postures, then this is the place to be.

LINKEDIN: This represents the boardroom of the online world, a more formal place to make professional work connections. That's pretty obvious from the look and feel of this platform, with everybody keen to show their best face. The groups and communities here can be useful to get your name out especially if you have a clear and defined interest, such as yoga, or nutrition, or writing.

GOOGLE+: A relative newcomer, this is Google's own social media platform. It all seems a bit clunky at times but it's free and there are some valuable additional benefits to bear in mind. For starters, anything you post here is supposed to carry extra punch in terms of SEO because it's Google's own platform. Also, people love the 'Hangouts' facility here, where you can effectively hold free, live online video chats and meetings, a great way to reach out to people in real-time even if they're on the other side of the world.

TWITTER: On Twitter you post micro 'tweets' of up to 140 characters (not words). This one bemuses many people at first, as they scan through page after page of seemingly inane and incomprehensible

learn from yesterday

messaging, although it's arguably the easiest one to master. With all the @ and # symbols going on, it can look awfully confusing, but you soon get used to it. Mainly text-based (it appeals to literary types) but it's fine to post pictures too. Tends to be fast moving and less formal than the others.

PINTEREST: On Pinterest, users 'pin' photos, quotes and other things like infographics to their boards, like a virtual pin board. There's lots of beautiful yoga imagery there, which can be linked back to your website, and it's also a good place to flag up healthy recipes, pretty sunsets and amazing studio interiors (and most other things too). There are some jaw dropping photos to be seen but it arguably lacks the immediacy and contact of some of the other platforms. Very popular though.

SNAPCHAT: This is another relatively new one and a little bit different too. Users post short videos and send to others for a one-time only viewing; the videos are then deleted. Odd, possibly, but it's very popular with the younger crowd. Lots of fun potential here, but not necessarily the most promising for promoting your business (although your creative application is the key, as always).

TUMBLR: This is another image-led community, popular with everyone from yoga superstars to porn stars. Again, like all the other platforms, you're looking to connect with your audience, and build up your community. It's also possible to use Tumblr as your main calling card, instead of, or alongside, a formal external website.

YOUTUBE: People love video. A lot of yoga instructors have their own YouTube channel and it can be a great way to get your name out there in a truly dynamic way. In today's fast-paced world, video is extremely appealing and highly engaging. It might not directly make you money but it might help grow your name and profile to bring new people into your class. If you can embed a little video taster on your website that's a great thing (provided it's of decent quality). Be warned: if you're not great on video then don't make videos. We can't all be movie stars. The last thing you want is to undermine yourself with a poorly made recording that makes you look amateurish. Stick to other stuff if that's the case, be honest with yourself and play to your strengths. There are other live video alternatives too such as Skype, Pow Wow, and Google+ Hangouts.

"Some yogis have gone on to build enormous followings via their Instagram accounts"

Cheryl MacDonald (UK)

FRANCHISING

THE YOGABELLIES CREATOR SAYS A FRANCHISE IS A GREAT WAY FOR NEW TEACHERS TO ESTABLISH THEMSELVES

Paying the bills | Yogabellies provides everything yogis need from the perspective of a socially-conscious business to make sure teaching yoga can bring home enough to pay the bills and more.

It can be hard starting out | The main problem with a basic yoga teacher training is you are given all of these beautiful yoga skills and then left at the end wondering what to do with them. There were almost 50 people on my original teacher training course and only four of them now teach yoga. Most people start a class, nobody comes, and then they can't afford to go on.

A franchise can be a solution | We take care of all the business side (websites, marketing, PR, social media), and even help our teachers with their business plan. I don't have any teachers who don't have full classes right now. We also give our teachers yoga business coaching on an ongoing basis to allow them to be professional, as well as ethical.

People find it empowering | I love what we have built here at YogaBellies: a community of women supporting women during the most important time of their lives (pregnancy) using yogic techniques.

Teachers love the community aspect | The thing teachers love the most is the day-to-day contact we all have across the world through our amazing support network. So, even though you work alone, you have friends ready to help and advise.

It can be very rewarding | Personally, I want to keep learning about yoga, especially for women and children, and to keep training teachers and encourage them on their teaching journey. I love the beautiful circle of compassion that we have built here with Yogabellies and anything more that comes from that makes me very happy.

make a difference

*"Yogabellies provides everything yogis need...
to make sure teaching can bring home enough
to pay the bills and more"*

'Help, I can't get enough students'

DON'T PRESS THE PANIC BUTTON IF YOUR CLASSES ARE HALF EMPTY. IT'S ALL PART OF THE **LEARNING** CURVE

If you're still struggling, and it's all getting a bit too much, and you're not seeing any interest in what you're offering, then maybe it's time to step back and have a re-think.

You may need to revise your expectations. Success rarely comes overnight (although it can) so be prepared for the long-haul. But if you're serious about this business then you know that already, and you won't mind taking a step back to move forward.

Take some time away. In fact, go for a walk in the woods, do some amazing yoga, hang out on the beach for a while. Breathe in the air.

When you're refreshed, start to look anew at your marketing options. You may be missing something very simple. Perhaps you're pitching to the wrong clientele. Go over the basics again. Don't be afraid to start afresh. It shows maturity if you can dust yourself down and begin again.

Here are a few marketing 'get out of jail' tips if you're struggling to make any headway.

1: KNOW YOUR COMMUNITY
In traditional marketing spiel this simply means getting to know the customer. It's boring and it's a cliche but your chances of selling something go up dramatically if you have this insight to hand. Who are your target students; what are the demographics (young or old, male or female)? Keep the pool as large as you can but try and identify some niches as well if possible.

2: KNOW THE COMPETITION
There's little point offering something identical to the successful and established teacher or studio nearby, unless you know that you can do it better or cheaper. Offer something that's at least slightly different (or be better and cheaper if you can't).

3: DON'T OVERSELL
Remember that customers (your potential students) are bombarded with marketing messages these days: billboards, TV, online, radio. They're tired of being 'sold to'. Although it's to be expected if you're selling cars or vacuum cleaners, you don't need it when it comes to yoga. Get your pitch right and you can use it sparingly but it can still be effective.

4: CONSULT THE EXPERTS
No, I don't mean hire a business guru (I know some teachers that do

and it's really not worth it), just talk to friendly faces that you know (yoga teachers, studio owners, friends and family). Ask them how they think you should go about it. Show them your previous marketing efforts and find out what they think.

5 : BEST OF BOTH WORLDS
Use both emotional and rational arguments to demonstrate what you are selling and why people need it. People come to yoga for all sorts of reasons. One of the big ones is that they just enjoy it. Luckily, it's also incredibly good for your general health and wellbeing too. Make sure people know they get all this - and more - when they come to your class.

6 : KEEP THE SHOPFRONT IMMACULATE
Maybe it seems shallow but presentation is so important. Make sure your shopfront (whether that's your website, a flyer, or a business card) is immaculate. It generates trust and builds confidence if your marketing material is professional. Lots of teachers and studios know this. Unfortunately, there are lots of people working within the general holstic healthcare realm that do not.

7 : NURTURE RELATIONSHIPS
Invest time getting to know any key players in your area that could

potentially help you out. You should do this anyway but it's a good starting point if you're stuck for students. Take time to befriend studio owners over a cup of coffee; nurture links with the local gazette.

8 : REVISIT YOUR SOCIAL MEDIA
Get some feedback too on your social media output. Compare what you're doing with those teachers that you admire. Copy them (discretely) if you have to. And donÐt neglect your website either. Keep it fresh.

9 : NETWORKING
It's not what you know, it's who you know. The oldest small business trick in the book is still just as valid as ever, so rub shoulders with people that mix in your circles (in studios or health clubs). Go to local business networking events too. They might be dull but itÐs a great way to meet other like-minded entrepreneurs (and potential sources of help in areas like social media, writing and other marketing skills).

10 : OFFER THE BEST SERVICE
There's little point going to all these lengths if your end product is no good. So make sure you back up any marketing claims with a high quality service, not just during your actual classes, but before (in your administration, bookings) and after (follow up, feedback).

"Use emotional and rational arguments to show what you're selling and why people need it."

How I made it happen

CHANGE-MAKER FAITH HUNTER IS REPRESENTING WOMEN OF COLOUR IN THE GLOBAL YOGA COMMUNITY

You need a mix of skills and talents | I think the main ingredients are the ability to work hard, diversity in the services you offer, creativity and thinking outside the box. Also, being strategic in your actions, openness to explore new opportunities, staying true to your purpose to serve, and the commitment to always be yourself.

I love my work | The best thing: continuing to show up fully in the world, and representing women of colour in the yoga community. Oh, and having the opportunity to travel the world and teach what I love: yoga.

I've had some big career moments | Appearing on the covers of Yoga Journal (twice), OM, Sweat Equity, and Origin, and being featured in many other magazines around the globe. Having videos online, teaching at the White House and at the world's largest yoga class in New York's Central Park. All of it is pretty cool.

There have been many highlights | They include: being of service and training 14 Haitian young adults that are currently becoming yoga teachers as part of my personal seva work. That, and creating yoga teacher training programmes that have been attended by students from around the world.

The yoga industry has changed | With the explosion of social media, the major shift has been the ability of teachers to respond and think strategically about their online presence. There's a high demand and need for teachers to not only teach locally, but if you desire to expand your reach, you have to create an online presence and consistently cultivate an online relationship with your social media community. The yoga teaching principles haven't changed; the way we share information has transformed.

Faith Hunter USA

show love

best advice:

Be clear about your goals and personal objectives. Understand fully your purpose for teaching yoga, and stay true to your personal core values.

#7

Amazing workshops & retreats

"*Yoga is almost like music in a way; there's no end to it*"

Sting

enjoy simplicity

*An idea is
only an idea until
you make it
happen*

Growing your business

THINK OF **DESIGNING** YOUR WORKSHOPS AND RETREATS AS THOUGH YOU'RE **CREATING** THE PARTY OF THE CENTURY

Workshops and retreats are excellent ways to grow your business.

This is confidence-building time for you as a new(ish) teacher, so don't bite off more than you can chew. Start small. Think workshops first, before exotic retreats. Costs are lower and so too are expectations, and that equates to less pressure.

One small but successful event with lots of happy, smiley faces at the end will nurture your confidence; one big retreat that ends badly may shatter it.

It's just common sense; feel your way as you go, getting an inclination for what your students require, how you can best help them, and, just as importantly, their appetite and ability to pay for it all. Ultimately, it's all about keeping an eye on costs and getting enough students to sign up for your idea, whether that's a short arm balance workshop in Warrington or a luxe fortnight in Florida.

So start small and get those bums on mats, without breaking the bank. What could be simpler? But it's got to be fun too. Think of it as like creating a party that you're going to invite guests (students) to: turn your workshops/retreats into an irresistible offer they simply can't turn down. Designing workshops and retreats, no matter how modest, should be fun. Yes, there's a business goal behind it, but let your imagination fly; don't limit your creative thinking.

After all, you're creating a party. So make sure it's one that you'd want to go to yourself.

Easy tiger

Yes, I know you want to host that magical Maldives retreat, but we've all got to start somewhere. If that $5,000 holiday in paradise seems too far off, then slap it on your vision board. Do it today right now. Just don't book your flights yet.

Working out workshops

LET'S GET THIS **PARTY** STARTED THEN, SHALL WE?

Workshops can help you grow your yoga business, support your students on their journey, and, with a little thought and planning, make a bit of extra cash for you too. And they're not too scary either for the newbie teacher. Like most things in life, to be excellent at this game you have to put the hours in. And that means preparation, planning and some legwork.

But where do you start?
When you're thinking up workshop ideas, especially if it's your first one, it's reassuring to know you're offering something due to popular demand.

Try to think of what your students want or need. Ask them if you have no idea.

Think about what would really help them. If they're yoga regulars and are desperate to learn inversions, then why not run an inversion workshop; that's your first one right there.

If they're always looking for more meditation or quiet time in your busy after-work class, then think about doing that.

Give them something they want and that will entice them to come along.

Most of all, give it some thought. If you know your students well, thats fine, but if you're in a new location then you might want to do some research first.

If in doubt, keep it simple. The last thing you need is to throw in a heavy Kirtan session to a group of Women's Institute beginners. It ain't gonna work.

Location: Think carefully about the time and place for your workshop. It's got to be close enough to be accessible for your students. Avoid rush hour and make sure the location is as easy to reach as possible. Think through the whole experience from your students' perspective. It may be a wonderful venue you've found but if the journey is too long or stressful then it could negate any other benefits.

Venue: For the most part it makes sense to stick to the usual places. Your local studio where you normally get together is just fine unless you can find something amazing. Doing a workshop inside a recognised local studio makes life a lot easier since all the facilities are on site and available and it's familiar to students. Still, if you can bag a great venue on the cheap for the day (or a weekend) that's fine as it'll seem like a mini retreat.

smile at strangers

Plan ahead: Plan well in advance. Give students as much notice as you can before the event - at least a few weeks, preferably more - so they can put it in their diary and plan ahead. That means early marketing is key. Get your flyers out and actively promote the event anywhere you can (including social media). Include essential details (time, cost, location), as well as a link to your website or Facebook page for further information.

Time of day: Think about the time of day, whether it will be dark or light outside, and how long you want the experience to last for. This is important when people start working out their travel time (which should be an essential part of your planing mix). If it's rush hour time they might well just say 'forget it'.

When: Avoid weekday workshops as people tend to be too busy with work and life. They're more available and relaxed at weekends. They'll look forward to it more on a Saturday or Sunday as they won't have to squeeze it in around work hours, or dropping the kids off at school. Bank Holiday weekends are not so good though as people tend to disappear or make other plans.

Duration: If you're planning a full day workshop then you'll need far more content (and varied content too, plus break times for food and chat) than you would for a three-hour get together. Three hours is a great length for workshops. People also love four hours, while two hours may be a little short. Attention spans can be pretty slim these days. All-day events are more of a niche (and more costly for you to produce in terms of time and money), and that's true obviously for two-day weekend events as well.

The takeaway: Make sure your students feel like they have learned something when they leave after the event. That means don't overload them with too much information. Think about a few key points and make sure these messages get through and are reinforced throughout the workshop. If people can learn a new skill during your event then they will consider it worthwhile and be more likely to book on to future workshops. Always send the troops home happy.

"Make sure your students feel like they have learned something when they leave after the event. Always send the troops home happy"

YOGA ROCKSTAR TIP #13

'SEE THE FUNNY SIDE'

"Have a sense of humour. Humour relaxes us, cuts through ego and changes us energetically"

Michele Pernetta | UK

Getting creative

REMEMBER THIS **WORKSHOP** BUSINESS SHOULD ALWAYS BE ABOUT LEARNING AND **FUN**

Have fun thinking up ideas for your party/workshop. In fact, have a real party to come up with ideas. Involve your friends, family, students. Have a brainstorming session. Scribble all the mad stuff down on a pad and go through it later.

You definitely want to create a good theme for your event, something that really calls to your people, or that will help them. Assess their needs and decide what aspect would help them the most. If you know they can't do Crow pose - and they want to - then bingo. Remember, its not about you showing off your abilities, it's about helping them to master their own.

Be specific: think arm balances, or inversions, or yoga for runners. This way, people know precisely what to expect when they walk through the door, minimising any chance of disappointment.

Take into account expectations too: so don't go offering 'The Best Yoga Workshop In The World' unless you want to disappoint your guests (plus it's far too vague). Keep it achievable and realistic and don't promise something you can't deliver.

Anytime of year is fine for workshops (although I've heard that September, October and November tend to be great months) but do take into account local factors and climate.

The name game
It can be a big selling point if you have a nice, catchy name for your workshop, so put your headline writing skills into practice. Really go to town on this one, and thrash out some wild names that might help sell your workshop idea.

The time of year is a good place to start. So, during the summer months, think more 'Summer Loving' style themes, whereas in December you can include some sort of Christmas concept. In January, 'Sticking to New Year's Resolutions' themes are popular, or maybe 'Four Heart Opening Moves for Valentines Day' when February 14 comes around. This could be a way to entice couples through the door as an alternative date night. The options are limitless. Let your mind play.

Yoga business workshops are also popular these days. Tap into on-trend cultural themes, as well, like movies, music, TV shows and see how you can spin that into a catchy name for a workshop. Glam it up and go to town. Paste a picture of a rock star on your flyer. Get people excited about your party so that they want to come.

best advice:

Be clear about your own motivation and keep it up. Personally, I need to enjoy my own practice, keep on learning, and sharing the benefits of yoga, especially to people with MS. This is the driving force that motivates me.

love is everything

Get Inspired

FIND THE DRIVING FORCE THAT REALLY MOTIVATES YOU, SAYS VERONIQUE GAUTHIER

Yoga has really helped with my MS | I started yoga in 2001 when I was diagnosed with MS. It helped me develop strength and flexibility, without making my symptoms worse. I was hooked. After my initial training in Vinyasa, I went to India for advanced training in yoga therapy to share my experiences.

I want to build my yoga therapy practice | In my classes, the focus is on self-discovery. This leads to empowerment, which is the first step to healing. Whether I teach yoga therapy for MS or for other conditions, I encourage students to investigate the relationship between their breath and their body, or their emotions.

I see myself as a guide | I can point students to a certain direction but they have the power to make the necessary changes. We then work together to explore the tools yoga therapy offers to find out what works best for them.

You don't have to have a niche | People choose their yoga classes for various reasons (price, location, recommendation), and they stay if they enjoy the class. This is the most important factor. However, having a niche can be useful, especially in yoga therapy. Students generally feel more at ease with a teacher who specialises in their own condition.

Be honest with yourself | No matter what your motives, money does matter. If you want to make a living, then accept that part of the job includes marketing and advertising, whether you like it or not. And we need to compromise. I wish I could teach yoga therapy for free but unfortunately it is not feasible; I have to be realistic.

Always keep on learning | I find it useful to read and learn more about the art of teaching and assisting, and not just about yoga.

Veronique Gauthier FRANCE

Workshop planning

THE SMALL THINGS MATTER WHEN IT COMES TO ORGANISING **BRILLIANT** WORKSHOPS

It calls for a sensible head to put together a successful workshop.

Think it through in terms of timing and location: parking, transportation, rush hour. What's the totality of the experience going to be like for your 'guests'?

The time of day matters: Saturday 2-4pm is a tried and tested two hour slot. That way you've got the whole morning to yourself, and you've still got the whole evening ahead of you when you get out. As a guide, 2pm is way better than 1pm; and a 4pm finish is way better than a 5pm finish. Duration may depend on who your audience is. For beginners, a three-hour workshop is still fine, but probably not four hours (or more). You can definitely get your message across in a three hour session, and still squeeze in a short 10-15 minute break (be precise: stick to that 1.15 pm-1.25 pm timeout!). To get the energy and creativity up if people are flagging then take an activity break, say, a bit of fun, shamanic drumming to shake up the room.

Next, divide your time into hour-long blocks.

It depends what you're teaching, of course, but for a three-hour show, the time could be split: one- third talking time (educational, background, instructional), and two-thirds practical and experience time (yoga and meditation).

If you've got a day-long workshop to plan, then divide it into two three-hour blocks, plus an extra hour for lunch. This turns a daunting one day workshop into manageable bite-size pieces.

Be realistic too: you must allow for the unexpected. It takes time for people to get to know each other and say hello; there's a centering to get everyone grounded and feeling comfortable; some people will show up late. Then there are those people who just need to 'check in' with you ('I've got a sore back so I need to modify', or 'I'm just a beginner, go easy with me') so allow time for that too. All of these things will happen, so plan for them.

How much?

WHAT'S THIS GOING TO COST AND WILL I MAKE ANY MONEY OUT OF IT?

The cheaper your workshop is the more people you're likely to interest; the more costly it is, the less people. You have to find the right balance.

Working out the correct price point is not an exact science but there are some ways to take out the guesswork. The starting point should always be your costs. How much will you need to make to recover all of your costs (your time, venue hire, printed materials/flyers, catering)?

Once you've done that, think about how much you want to make out of the event. What would make it worth your time? You should be aiming to make hundreds of pounds from any workshop to make it worthwhile. Charging £45 for a three hour workshop is a reasonable sum. If you get 10 people along then that's £450. But you'll need to deduct all of your expenses too.

Figuring out costs: This starts with your venue. You can host a workshop almost anywhere but your local studio is probably the safest place to start, as there are friendly, supportive faces around, and all the equipment and facilities are already there.

If you're new to the area, get to know studio owners before pitching a workshop idea to them. Try a few classes first if you have to. If you're friendly with the owners then they'll be more inclined to let you use their premises.

Of course, you'll also need to split the take if you're using someone else's studio. Usually this is either an agreed flat fee or on a shared 50/50 take of the proceeds. This sliding scale changes for big or recognised teachers (edging up to 70/30 in favour of the teacher). In this case, the studio is often more than happy just to be associated with a leading yoga name, as they know they can put bums on mats. Plus, of course, their fee may well be higher anyway (£75+ per person for a workshop led by a top name is normal).

Remember that a studio will need to deduct tax from any workshop revenues. And they'll probably expect cash on the day too. You must agree any expenses in advance with your studio partners (promotional, marketing, catering costs), so there are no nasty surprises or potential money disputes later on.

Offers: if you're doing two events on one day (one in the morning, one in the afternoon), you could offer reduced prices for people booking both. Charge a little extra if you're planning to throw in some lunch (that's another cost you need to factor in).

Teaching tips

IT'S NOT ALL ABOUT YOU: **EMPOWER** YOUR **STUDENTS** ON THEIR YOGA JOURNEY

Remember: this workshop is for the students not for you. You want to empower them and to inspire them, to lift their practice up to the next level. For the most part, that means pitching it all well within their comfort zone and current level of understanding.

You should probably aim to do most of it, say 90%, in the 'comfort zone', and perhaps only 10% in their 'growth edge'. Don't push them too much. If you give them eight things to remember or do in three hours they'll probably get confused, so don't overload them.

Think about what your top three priorities for the session are: What you're aiming to do is to empower them to do it for them themselves (be it a headstand or mindfulness meditation), otherwise they'll still be dependent on you even after the workshop.

Try and get the first half of the session to support the second half learning. It's really powerful to watch students getting better at something during the day.

And don't forget the 'takeaway' - the message that students will take away with them. The following week, get your students to apply it all at their next class. Aim for them to execute precisely what was covered in the workshop.

This is not just a space for you to entertain (or show off). You want your 'guests' to take home practical skills, and, hopefully, to have a bit of fun and connection in the process.

Whatever you're planning, it's essentially much the same model across the yoga, Pilates and fitness world.

Marketability

WITHOUT GOOD MARKETING YOUR **FANTASTIC WORKSHOP** MAY ALL BE FOR NOTHING

Set yourself up for success. If your marketing is good, people will want to come to your party. Your event has got to appear desirable to your target audience. Who are you aiming the workshop at? Are there enough of these people? Be specific, yes, but equally, try and frame it to appeal to a broad range of people.

Marketing is mostly about creativity, common sense and perseverance. If you're partnering with a studio then you can expect additional marketing oomph from them, although the primary effort should always be you.

Raising some money for charity is a good way to get the numbers up. Yes, this may eat into your own earnings, but it's a good win-win for everyone; it feels good knowing your helping others. It doesn't even have to be a small percentage cut of your take, you could just put a collection box out for students to donate at the end of the gig.

There are so many tools to help you promote your workshops (websites, flyers, social media, email bulletins). Use them all. Think up special offers and incentives too. Early bird booking discounts are a great way to get the ball rolling from the start.

Workshop flyers: Good flyers don't just provide information, they also provide inspiration. Give yours a short and snappy title (remember that headline writing?) and put in a call to action: 'you need this workshop and you need it now'. Use statistics to support your sales pitch. Let people see your face as well (people buy into people, not just facts and figures).

Make them double sided. You can include information on one side, and maybe a cool, inspirational image on the other. Give a snapshot of the content but don't overload people with detail. Three main benefits is good. Oh, and you don't need to include maps (we now have Google maps on our phones), nor your life story (that's all on our website, remember?).

And, needless to say, put your flyers up well in advance. You'll massively increase chances of success this way.

Get people to email you from the flyer if possible. That way you can collect their email address for some cross marketing later on. Think big too: never do 100 flyers. Do several thousand. And then get rid of them very quickly. Go out and really sell your wonderful workshop rather than leave it chance.

YOGA ROCKSTAR TIP #14

'KEEP INSPIRATIONAL COMPANY'

"Surround yourself
with inspirational people.
Spend less time with
people that drain
your energy"

Jo De Rosa | UK

pay it forward

Your first yoga retreat

IT MAY SEEM A DAUNTING LEAP BUT MANY OF THE **STRATEGIES** USED FOR **CREATING** WORKSHOPS CAN BE APPLIED HERE TOO

Retreats may be on a different scale to workshops, but it's still all about managing costs, doing your sales and marketing, thorough planning and preparation.

The goal is to make your retreat enjoyable and successful for students (as well as you) and of course to make it profitable.

It's true, you're not going on holiday here, you're working. Leading a retreat can be a challenging time for the new teacher; you'll be holding space for people which brings pressures and responsibilities. Still, now you're a successful, practicing yoga instructor and you're off to a nice location, helping others to relax and enjoy themselves, to deepen their yoga experience – so why shouldn't you be having some fun as well?

There's a subtle difference, of course. For participants, the retreat may well be purely a holiday, a chance to do yoga daily, eat healthy food and leave their troubles behind; it's a time of rejuvenation and transformation for them.

For you, a retreat is not a holiday. It's also very different from teaching a single class back home. You'll need a wider set of skills and resources to draw on. Nonetheless, if you've done your homework, then just tap into that positive group energy vibe and you'll be glowing by the end of the week too.

Pack your bags

ASK YOURSELF: WHY DO YOU WANT TO RUN A RETREAT?

Your motives are really important here. Some teachers specifically want to spend time away with their students to help them deepen their practice. Others might see it as a way to finance their annual vacation. Do you want to make money out of the retreat, or is it a means to get others to pay for your holiday? Is it just for fun? You've got to be sure of your motivations.

This will help when it comes to marketing your retreat. It's a highly competitive field so you need to be absolutely clear on this. What is it you're offering students and why should they book with you? If you're new, without a huge pool of loyal students, it's a tough ask to get the numbers up.

Your motivations will guide you when it comes to planning things. You're inviting people to come with you on a big yoga party. It needs to be a compelling offer in order to get them to hand over their hard earned cash.

And it's not always enough to offer great yoga in a great location - there are countless other fantastic teachers doing the same thing. Students have immense choice when it comes to deciding their holidays. Even if they choose to go on a yoga retreat (rather than kayaking in Colorado, or road cycling in Spain), why should they go away with you?

Convincing a potential student to sign up for your retreat is a tough assignment. It's much harder than getting a student to sign up for your class back home, since the costs and commitment required are much greater.

If you understand your motivations early on it will help you to get the balance right in the way you describe and market your retreat. And this is essential in securing bookings.

HOLIDAY VIBE

Work out what sort of retreat vibe you want. Some groups are definitely more on the holiday side while others can be more formal. Are you heading out for a strict detox to escape the world and its sinful ways, or are you happy to party on? Don't get too puritanical on your clients, let them have their coffee and booze if they want it (yoga's all about allowing and accepting, right?) unless of course you are on a special detox; that's different. Most people don't abuse these privileges. Heck, if folks wanted to rave all night, they probably wouldn't be on a yoga break at all, but living it up at some grand Ibiza foam party.

follow your bliss

SO HOW DO YOU START PLANNING YOUR GREAT YOGA GETAWAY?

It's certainly possible to make money out of retreats, but start with some brutal self-analysis. Begin with the question of whether you are truly ready to run a retreat. Ask yourself with absolute honesty if you have the experience and knowledge to lead and to take responsibility for your students' wellbeing for a whole weekend, week or even a fortnight? Do you really know what you're getting yourself into? Talk to experienced teachers to hear how it all works. It takes a certain amount of maturity and selflessness to run a retreat well. These are not necessarily things that are age-related; it depends on the individual. If you're sure you want to proceed then lets think details.

Timing: start with the timing of your retreat. When will you host the retreat? Timing can be a determining factor in success or failure. What about school holidays? If it's during school holiday time then flight costs go up. However, if it's term-time, when children are at school, parents with kids might not be able to come. It's a trade off that you'll have to make.

Location: the weather in your chosen place is obviously important. If it's guaranteed sunshine then you're more likely to pull in the punters. In Europe, the months of November, December, January, February and even March are the typical low season, when the weather is cooler. This means that venue prices and flights may be cheaper, but getting guests is harder.

Extras: as a rule, try to provide the bare minimum for people. That sounds harsh but it'll make your life easier. Just hire the venue if possible (which usually charges a per head fee) so you don't get bogged down in too much detail, which would drain your time (and probably your enthusiasm). You must agree any expenses with your chosen venue or partners in advance.

Double up: you can recruit help along the way with a second teacher. It's nice not to go it alone, but there are cost implications. If you bring in a second teacher it may be hard to make any money from the retreat because of the second set of expenses (flights, accommodation); the budget then starts to shoot up.

Practical considerations

HERE ARE SOME **THINGS** THAT YOU ARE GOING TO HAVE TO **CONSIDER** ALONG THE WAY

Venue: This is the big one. Where exactly will your retreat be held? You need to select a location and a venue. This will, of course, impact cost. Ease of transportation is critical here. It might be a nice idea to host your retreat in Fiji but how many of your potential students will be able to afford it? The closer to home, and the easier the access, the more likely you will get the numbers.

Don't be shy when it comes to asking questions. The ease and frequency of communication with the retreat centre may be indicative of its efficiency.

What's their reputation like with other teachers? Ask a venue for references. It's ideal (but not always possible) to check a venue out before you book your group trip. No wonder many teachers return to the same place year after year once they've identified a venue they like. Befriend the management and staff: it'll really help you, and could have a positive effect on the overall experience of your guests. It's always worth negotiating here although many centres are themselves as much a labour of love as they are businesses, and don't earn huge profits, so tread lightly.

Facilities: Know exactly what the yoga room is like (and what props and equipment are available). Check out the photos. What other facilities do you need: wifi, swimming pool, sauna?

Rooms: This will form part of your decision on the venue. What accommodation is on offer? Are we talking dorm style or private rooms? En suite or shared bathrooms? Toilets where you can flush the paper or do you have to stick it in a bin (common

in many remote, rural European establishments)? Who is going to assign students to their rooms (you or the centre)? Are your likely guests going to be okay with sharing rooms? If you're targeting the high-end market then they'll expect high quality facilities and their own rooms. The independent traveling 19-year-old yogini, however, might be on a budget and only too keen to pair up with a roommate. Again, this means you've got to know your target market.

yes you can

Food: This can make or break a retreat so be sure to check out food references with other teachers if you can. Find out what's on offer. Do they cater for special needs (vegan, gluten-free)? Will snacks, teas and drinking water be available, and will they be free of charge? Make sure meal times fit in with your proposed yoga schedule. Don't underestimate this. It's vital that people enjoy their food while they're away.

Travel: If you're doing as little as possible then you definitely don't want to mess around with flights. You're not a travel agent. If there is flying involved you need to check flight availability and distance and transfer options from the centre to the airport. Sometimes transfers can add a whole extra expense so if you can help minimise this (through co-ordinating transportation) then that's great.

Checklist

Daily Schedule:
• Asana practice times •
• Other group activities •
• Where and how often is free time •
• Massage and therapy treatment time •
• Meal times •
• Evening activities •

Transportation:
• Make an arrival sheet for students (with flight times and phone numbers) •
• And who collects (a driver; group member)? •
• Departure schedule •
• Multiple shuttle/pick-up times or just one? •

Marketing:
• Postcards/flyers (what details to include: what, when, where, how much) •
• Email lists •
• Online tools (Facebook, Google Ads) •
• Local community outreach •
• Do you offer group rates? •
• Discounts for yoga studio members? •

Insurance:
• Travel waiver (search online for a basic form) •
• Liability waiver •
• Cancellation policy •
• Where are local hospitals/emergency plan •

Getting the numbers

DON'T UNDERESTIMATE THE TASK OF **ATTRACTING** SUFFICIENT **STUDENT** NUMBERS TO YOUR **RETREAT**

Just because people are asking about your retreat does not mean they are going to sign up. Confirmation and payment is all that counts.

Even if many of your students do genuinely want to go away with you and chill out in the Andalusian sunshine that doesn't necessarily mean they will. Sometimes they can't get the time off work; maybe their grandmother is poorly.

Do be realistic about your pulling power, especially as a new teacher, and do consider the relative affluence (or lack of) among your pool of students.

Once you're a yoga rock star pin-up you can feel more comfortable about this (and charge more) but for now keep it real and be realistic.

Keep track of who has paid what and when. It's okay if you want to cut people some slack if they need extra time to pay but keep an eye on your own commitments to pay the retreat centre. Make sure you don't get yourself in a difficult position if you are relying on guest payments to meet the centre fees. As always, the numbers have got to add up.

A pain in the butt

Unfortunately, a lot of people tend to book at the last minute. This makes financial planning even more fraught. Also, a lot of venues want to be paid cash. Fine if you're in the same country, but not fine if you're heading out overseas and need a different currency. Just be prepared for all this money stuff.

set high standards

The wow factor

HERE ARE SOME **SIMPLE** WAYS TO TURN YOUR RETREAT FROM ORDINARY TO **EXTRAORDINARY.**

Welcome all: make your students feel welcome and safe right from the start. If you can, get to know who is coming before arrival and find out what their goals and expectations are.

Accommodation: make sure your students know what to expect from the venue. Are they okay sharing bathrooms or rooms; being up in the hills; having no wifi?

Opening ceremony: on the first day, it's good to include an opening circle to mark the start of a retreat. Use a talking stick or crystal to pass around to make it more fun, so all can speak without interruption. Simple introductions help create bonds.

Free time: be sure to include some free time during the week. It's nice to keep students engaged but you don't want to overwhelm them. They'll end up exhausted.

Good karma: charity adds an extra dimension to things, and you don't have to allocate money either. Maybe there's a local good cause you could all help with during the week.

Day trips: optional but if there are spectacular sights nearby then it can be a great way to facilitate the group experience.

Transitional moments: be sensitive to emotional mood shifts, such as a few days in when people start to get into the flow, or towards the end as they think about going home.

Special occasions: celebrate birthdays and other events too, such as a new moon. Think music night or mantra singing. A campfire is always a great way to get the group together.

The last supper: do something special on the final night to 'close' the event before it's time to actually say goodbye. It may be a rush on departure day when there are flights to catch.

Closing remarks: create a sharing circle at the end where everyone can talk and express gratitude.

Keep in touch: keeping students connected after their holiday (by email or on Facebook) is a nice way of keeping the vibe going (and plugged into your future retreat plans). Send a 'thank you' by email and be sure to follow up on any topics discussed during the retreat (great websites, music, books).

The little things

RETREATS MAY BE A BIG PROPOSITION BUT IT'S THE SMALL STUFF THAT COUNTS IN THE END

PAY ATTENTION TO THE DETAILS
If the schedule ever changes, for whatever reason, make sure you tell the venue (especially the kitchen). You won't curry favour with the chef if you leave their sumptuous banquet going cold on the table. And keep all of your students informed too.

FAREWELLS ARE IMPORTANT
Check out the relevant departure times with your group so you're all prepared and make sure all personal expenses are settled with the retreat centre. A special last meal (last supper) makes for a proper send-off the night before.

DISAPPEARING ACT
And there's good etiquette for you to consider too. Leave with your guests, or after your guests, but not before them.

AND DON'T FORGET YOU
After all this attention on others, be certain to address your own needs as the teacher or leader as well. Know where your room is, be clear when practice times are. What are your boundaries for personal time and space at meals and free time? You've got to allocate at least some 'you time' into the schedule; you need a breather at some point.

FEEDBACK
This will be incredibly useful when planning your next retreat. Ask what people liked and didn't like.

Peter Simmons (UK)
BUSINESS CONSULTANT

LEADING A RETREAT REQUIRES MATURITY
AND BUSINESS ACUMEN. HERE ARE SOME
COMMON PITFALLS FACING THE UNWARY

This is work: a common problem arises when a teacher mixes their own wish to go on a retreat with the desire to run one. When they realise how much work is involved they often get disillusioned and cancel, possibly losing their deposit and letting students and the centre down in the process.

You need maturity: it's important to ask yourself if you really have enough experience and knowledge to lead a retreat well. Have you developed sufficiently as a teacher to take responsibility for your students' wellbeing for a week (or more)? It takes a certain amount of maturity (which is not necessarily age-related) and selflessness (which is definitely not age-related) to lead a retreat really well.

Double act: I often encourage newer teachers to team up with another teacher for their first retreat. This doubles the pool of students and means teachers can support each other in marketing, selling and delivering the retreat. Just make sure the terms of your partnership are agreed upfront, especially the financial details. Partnerships can be a great support mechanism, but they can be hellish if not clearly defined.

It's a business: a common mistake is the illusion that yoga is different to any other business, and that because you're bringing something good into the world, the world will look after you. This may be true on some cosmic level but I haven't seen any proof of it on the ground. The same laws of commerce apply just as reliably in the yoga world as in any other business. It's not enough just to be really enthusiastic and excited.

Timing is everything: the most successful retreat leaders plan a year to a year-and-a-half ahead. I think anything less than eight months is a bit crazy.

Nïkki Ralston NEW ZEALAND

embrase love

Get inspired

SINGLE MUM NIKKI RALSTON HAS SUCCESSFULLY COMBINED HER MASSAGE THERAPY SKILLS WITH YOGA TEACHING. SHE NOW RUNS HER OWN YOGA STUDIO IN AUCKLAND

Yoga was a natural progression | I'd been a massage therapist for 15 years so yoga teaching was a fairly natural progression. It was easy for me to translate my anatomical knowledge into yoga postures and communicate this to students in a really clear accessible way. I slowly started to build up my classes and private clients, and have done less massage work over time. Even today, I still do a few massages a week because I love working deeper with bodies to create lasting change.

New Zealand yoga is thriving The yoga market in New Zealand is rapidly emerging. Because of the smaller population (4.2 million) it's on a different scale to the US or the UK but I have seen it boom over the last few years. I have taught at Wanderlust in New Zealand and Australia, which has been hugely successful. I think that shows where yoga is at Down Under. However, we don't get as many international teachers over here so it's expensive for us to travel and up-skill our training elsewhere.

I'm doing my own thing | I have shifted away from my traditional Iyengar training and developed my own method (The Ralston Method), that's still rich in alignment, but light-hearted and playful. By going outside of tradition within a small community, it has been challenging but liberating. My long-term goal is to get yoga into schools, to create sustainable change for the future.

Find your authentic self | Finding your own authentic voice and trusting that you are enough is probably the hardest thing in establishing yourself as a teacher. It takes time to build up a following of dedicated students but if you keep sharing from your heart, and from what you know, you will slowly attract people who resonate with what you have to share.

I want to reach further afield | My Auckland studio was always meant to be a base so that I could travel more and teach workshops and retreats both in New Zealand and overseas, so that's all in the plan. We have such an amazing country here. I'd also love to bring more international teachers in to experience this beauty, and to help elevate the yoga community here.

best advice:
Know that your real learning starts when you begin to teach and work with lots of different bodies. It takes a while to find your own style and if you aren't used to working so closely with people you may find it exhausting at first.

Keep your energy up Enjoy your practice and keep going to other yoga classes. Find some techniques to keep your energy clear.

You do the math

WORK OUT ALL YOUR COSTS **FIRST,** BEFORE YOU FIX A **PRICE** FOR YOUR YOGA RETREAT

Before you can set a price for your retreat you need to work out your costs, starting with how much the venue hire is going to be. There are a lot of variables: will you pay on a per room/bed basis, or for the whole venue? Will meal costs be included in the total price for the venue? Then you need to think about other costs related to the venue, such as transfers to and from the airport. There are plenty of others:

Marketing and advertising: how much do you plan to spend on marketing your retreat? You must include everything (printing, bank/credit card transaction fees, advertisements).

Teaching costs: what are your own teaching costs and expenses (flights, travel, meals and lodging). Are you paying another teacher or any teaching assistants?

Potential extras: day trips, excursions and cultural events; money exchange charges; house tips for retreat centre staff; massage and therapy treatments; souvenirs and gifts for students.

Banks fees: make sure you include any transaction charges in your costs; there's often an extra charge when taking credit card bookings.

SOME BORING STUFF

As if that wasn't enough, there are some other bits of paperwork you'd be well advised to consider too:

Cancellations: it's a good idea to have a cancellation policy in place. Sometimes things just happen beyond our control. Cancellation works both ways. It's not just you that might need to pull the plug; students may (for very genuine reasons) need to withdraw from your retreat too. What's your refund policy going to be? Make sure it's all clearly stated and confirmed in writing (signed) by the student when booking.

Insurance: it costs money, and it's another expense, but you must have it. if you're going abroad, make sure your insurance covers you. Call your insurance firm and check with them. Make sure your students get cover too.

Liability: liability forms are a good idea too. Find a sample release form on the internet and have your students sign it. Yes, it'll probably all be fine, but teachers really do need to protect themselves.

Setting your price

HEY DIDN'T YOU KNOW? NUMBER CRUNCHING IS THE NEW **ROCK AND ROLL**

When you're working out your costs be conservative in projecting how many people will come on your retreat. It's also wise to over estimate how much things will cost you. List absolutely everything, then add some more.

After costs have been established, create different scenarios of how many students might attend to set the selling price. Divide the total expenses (including your own teaching fee) by these theoretical student numbers to find various selling prices. Find the break-even point for you, that's your baseline (based on a minimum number of guests). Each additional guest should, in theory, start to push you into more profitable territory.

Here's the thing: a lot of inexperienced retreat leaders wildly over estimate the numbers that will sign up to their gig. Many are so excited about 'their retreat' that they do not view it with the required degree of objectivity. Typically, somewhere in the mid-range, between your high estimates and low estimates, works best. Do look around first to see what others are charging, especially at your preferred venue, to make sure you're competitive.

Work through these very carefully if you're serious about running a profitable yoga retreat. Once you've got all that sorted (and that's a lot of work, planning, emails and maybe a few setbacks along the way) you can start to shape the feel of your retreat, making it unique and fabulous.

Marketing your retreat

HOW YOU 'SELL' YOUR RETREAT MAKES ALL THE DIFFERENCE

The market for retreats is much more competitive than it used to be. Even top teachers may struggle if they are slack on their marketing. It's all about converting interest into genuine bookings.

The most obvious pool of clients for your retreat is your existing student base.

Obviously, the more of a following you have the easier it is to attract people.

Celebrity yoga teachers can now pull in students from all over the world, people they've never met before. Unfortunately, there are not many teachers that can do this.

You may be able to tip the balance more in your favour with a strong online presence. This has become a great new way to build your profile from the comfort of your own bedroom.

Answer queries as soon as possible, and always within 24 hours, otherwise they'll look elsewhere.

Flyers: most of the same rules apply here. Get creative. Demand their attention. Get those flyers out!

Website: make sure the retreat is listed on your website and the venue's website. Set up a specific site just for that retreat (essentially an online flyer). If you like, to build additional excitement. Add a clock on there so people can count down until they jet off on holiday.

List your event everywhere: on yoga listing sites, most of which are free of charge.

Online advertising: this may work for big retreat centres but may be less of an option for individuals with tight budgets.

Go for specific yoga forums, websites, magazines - anywhere you know your target market will hang out. Wherever that is make sure that your retreat details can be found there.

Another key thing here is to describe the accommodation, food, location, bathroom arrangements as accurately as you can. This reduces the chance of leaving guests disappointed.

If you can't get your head around this marketing business (or can't be bothered) team up with a dedicated yoga holiday company (there are quite a few of them). Typically, they'll employ yoga teachers on a set fee and take care of the marketing and administrative side for you. If one of your students does decide to come then most of these companies will also pay you an extra commission.

What a swell party

LIKE ALL **GREAT** PARTIES, YOU WANT YOUR STUDENTS **BUZZING** AFTERWARDS – BUT WITHOUT THE HANGOVER

Just to recap: Think of your workshops and your retreats in terms of organising a party. So be sure to invite your people to a 'party' that they'll want to go to, and one they'll enjoy and benefit from. Once you've got them there, make sure it's an experience they'll never forget - for all the right reasons!

A lot of teachers teach things for no particular reason. Try and see some logic to it all, whatever it is you're doing (retreats or workshops), and dovetail it with your usual classes back home if possible. Make it all relevant to people

Above all, don't doubt yourself. Most yoga instructors know far more than they think they know. You've got the training, you've got the knowledge. Now share it with others.

Be well organised and attentive to your students' needs and you can't go too far wrong. Trust yourself, follow your heart, and lead by example.

Just keep an eye on the books as you're doing it.

best advice:

Make sure you have a recognised training and certification to fall back on, and that you have insurance cover, just in case. Stay grounded, keep focused: never let the ego take over, and make sure that you stay real.

you are unique

How I made it happen

KEEP IT REAL AND BE PREPARED FOR HARD WORK IF YOU WANT LONG-TERM SUCCESS

Maya Fiennes MACEDONIA

Stay honest and authentic | Be true to yourself. Have lots of patience and integrity in what you do. Make sure that what you offer is well considered and of a high standard.

There is no right way | Try to see the humour in it all. I've come to understand that the problem is when we all try to be perfect, and do things perfectly. When things don't go that way we take it personally and the result is stress. There is no right or wrong way, just whatever works for you.

Make yourself known | Use social media in a clever way and try to participate in as many yoga conferences and events as possible, especially at the start, to make yourself known.

I've had some incredible highs | The highlight of my yoga career was participating on stage at the biggest yoga event ever in Central Park, New York on July 16, 2010. The power of a big group (there were 10,000 mats) doing yoga and chanting mantras was the most satisfying feeling, and seeing the change of people's consciousness and the planetary shift, the energy rising in a big way, was an amazing experience.

Choose your partners wisely | Start from the bottom, work hard, and only make investments when you know that the return is highly probable. Try to find partners who have the financial means to support you, but make sure that those partners are solid and that any agreements are fair, reflecting the input of each partner.

8

The next level

(travel, video, teacher training)

"It's great to be here.
It's great to be anywhere."

Keith Richards

See beyond your limitations

So, what's next?

MAKE MOVIES, TRAVEL THE **WORLD** OR TRAIN OTHER TEACHERS: THE WORLD'S YOUR **OYSTER**

There's no chronology to any of this yoga business. So if you want to start making videos or selling your own cool yoga clothes straight after training then go for it. Why mess around with the other stuff?

Setting up your own teacher training course is a different story and typically requires a lot of experience, however. That's certainly the case for all the teachers in this book that have gone on to set up their own successful teacher training schools.

But that's not true in other niches, like shooting yoga videos, a great way to grow your brand. Anyone can do it, but follow a few simple bits of advice and you can produce your own highly professional content that students may well be willing to pay for.

Like most things in yoga, you're only really limited by your imagination as to what your next move will be. Maybe you want to run your own retreat centre in the sun, or combine teaching work with selling jewellery on the beach in Thailand. A yoga teaching certificate means you have a highly portable skill if you wish to travel the world.

Life's an adventure and your yoga toolkit gives you everything that you need to explore.

YOGA ROCKSTAR TIP #15
'LIVE THE JOURNEY'

'Be humble, be authentic
and be present. Really
live the journey, not just
in the yoga room"

Katy Appleton | *UK*

No rules

THERE ARE NO RULES WHEN IT COMES TO **YOGA CAREERS**. JUST FOLLOW YOUR **DREAMS**

Once you've got a yoga teaching certificate under your belt, there are so many possibilities. This book has followed a fairly standard, linear career path: picking up experience along the way in studios, evolving into areas like workshops and retreats and, coming next, owning your own studio.

But hey, what's normal? It doesn't have to be like that. The beauty of yoga is that it can be all things to all people; it's more about free thinking and creative expression. So don't be limited in your ideas and ambitions, there are so many other exciting routes to take.

Yoga is a definite career choice for many people, but for others, it's a nice-to-have string to your bow as you travel the world, or follow an alternative line of work. In other holistic health disciplines, like nutrition, or even coaching, a yoga qualification is the perfect complement to your work. It adds clout to your CV. Then, of course, there are those that train up purely for the love of yoga, with no intention of teaching as a career. It's all good.

So whatever direction you choose in life, having a yoga teaching training certificate is never going to hold you back. It is totally liberating. It opens doors.

A world of possibilities

FIND YOUR **NICHE:** WHAT ELSE CAN YOU DO WITH A YOGA TEACHING **QUALIFICATION?**

CLOTHING - The rise of yoga fashion means lots of creative yoga types are now producing their own boutique clothing for studio and leisure wear. Some of this yoga clothing - which ranges from workout gear and hippie sweaters, to sandals, bras and jewellery - is exquisite. It's typically produced by small, independent family manufacturers in developing countries. India is a popular choice. Powered by passion, these yoga designers link their fashion project to a local charity or community support initiative. It's a win-win for all: you're supporting a niche yoga firm by buying their clothes, money goes to charity, plus you get to look fab in your new kit. What more could you ask?

MUSIC - Music is the symphony of the soul. With lots of teachers using gentle music, kirtan, or other mellow sounds in their classes, it makes sense that many go on to make their own. It's a truly wonderful creative expression of who you are. There's no guarantee of making any real money out of it, but there are quite a few good examples of those that have done so and now sucessfully tour the world as recording artists.

It's also something that can be done on the cheap too, with the advent of professional music software on your laptop at home.

TRAVEL - Use your yoga teaching certificate as your passport to working around the world. For many new teachers, especially youngsters, yoga opens up a whole array of possibilities for working overseas. Check the rules and regulations wherever you go, but if you're exploring south-east Asia and certain other places then there's always a need for good yoga instructors. You may come across work as you travel; or scan social media for opportunities. And if you're not the backpacking type then get a gig as the resident yoga instructor on a cruise liner in the Caribbean. What a job!

EDUCATION - It's important to stay ahead of the curve and keep up-to-date with new techniques; it's even a condition when you're with one of the big yoga accreditation groups. For more experienced teachers, the potential exists to craft niche yoga courses in specialist areas like yoga therapy or yoga for sports. It has to be done right, and it has to be totally professional, but it can be an exciting route to take as you expand your business.

WRITING - Writing can be a great way for yoga students and teachers to stay creative, fresh and inspired. It's also a highly portable skill if you're traveling. It is possible to make money if you are good and you can find an outlet that will pay. Poetry is a popular choice too although it's hard to make any income from it. At the very least, keeping a journal is a great way to clear your thoughts and get it all down on paper.

BLOGGING - Computer says 'yes'. There are countless yoga blogs online these days. Some of them are great, some are awful. It's a great way to polish your writing skills and promote your name but don't expect it to lead to much paid work. It probably won't. Do it for fun, write what inspires you, and see where it all leads.

ART - If you're already handy with a brush, then yoga may bring out your artistic side even more. Even if you don't consider yourself 'arty', yoga has a funny way of getting the creative juices flowing. Like writing and blogging, it's hard to make any real money from this, but by no means impossible. Many yoga fans have created beautiful yoga-inspired artwork that sells very well, both as full size pictures or in smaller niche products like postcards.

YOGA EQUIPMENT - As well as clothing and fashion gear, many people go on to create yoga products that will help students either in the studio or in their home practice, from beautiful eye pillows, to mats, and yoga swings. The complexity (and cost) depends on what you're producing. At the top end, there are firms that now specialise in making heat and humidity systems for hot yoga studios. They aren't cheap. Still, if you've spotted a gap in the market, and think you have an idea for a product that could help others, then there's certainly money to be made here.

CHARITY - Many passionate yogis and yoginis devote their time to charitable work. This comes in all shapes and sizes, from giving it all up to work with the starving in Africa, to running monthly donation-based classes to help the local homeless project. It's easy to develop your yoga career in tandem with this, and a great way to keep you grounded and aligned with true yogic principles. You may not make any money, of course, but you're reputation as a human being will soar.

"If you've spotted a gap in the market, and think you have an idea for a product that could help others, then there's certainly money to be made"

Choices, choices, choices

WHERE DO YOU **WANT** TO GO WITH THE REST OF YOUR **LIFE?**

When you're thinking what to do next in life, especially if you're feeling stuck, the best thing you can do is hit the mat. Find some space before embarking on any bold endeavour to gain clarity.

Sometimes, it helps to think demographics in order to plot your next step. Working with children as a yoga teacher may be your dream job; for others, the idea of helping pro sportsmen and women fine tune their talent may appeal more. These are all valid options open to you now.

Yoga for seniors: you may still be recovering from your 21st birthday party hangover, but with an increasingly aging population in the West, this is going to be a huge area for yoga teachers in the future.

Yoga for children: at the other end of the age spectrum, teaching yoga to children and teenagers can be a magical and rewarding experience. Many schools are also now beginning to embrace the power of yoga.

Yoga therapy: the application of yoga for specific conditions, both physical and mental, is already popular in the USA, but lags behind in the UK. Yet here's a diverse group of people that arguably stand to benefit from yoga more than any other.

Yoga for sports: athletes are waking up to the potential of yoga for the competitive edge that it can provide. Likewise, yoga teachers are waking up to that potential opportunity.

Meditation

What about becoming a meditation expert. Or producing your own audio meditations to bring peace and calm to the masses. The Dalai Lama reckons we can bring about world peace if we all teach our kids to meditate. So let's do it. No wonder meditation training is on the up.

see the funny side

Get Inspired

YOGA TEACHER AND NUTRITION EXPERT CHARLOTTE WATTS HAS ALSO ACHIEVED SUCCESS AS A PUBLISHED AUTHOR

I've always enjoyed writing | Books seem to happen naturally for me. The main challenge is the time to do it. My latest, The De-Stress Effect is how I work; combining nutrition and yoga with mindfulness to help people find their best quality of life, free from the anxiety, mood issues, insomnia, that 'constant alert' can bring. I live and work this stuff so it comes naturally in my writing.

Yoga was a natural progression for me | Yoga and nutrition played equal parts in my own journey back to health, so one without the other seemed incomplete. Bringing the two together in books and on retreats (as I do now) feels like I'm finally creating the experience I hoped others could have.

I've always had different income streams | I mix and match according to practical needs, energy and where I need my focus to be at any given time; I wouldn't want to rely on yoga teaching too much. I am keen that yoga is accessible, non-elitist. I don't want to care how many students turn up, I just want to give full attention to those who are there so other income sources are key to that.

I never had a grand plan | But I am future-driven and always looking for the next thing. I'm finally getting to a point where I feel I have all the pieces in place and now I'm able to relax and let them shape with more ease. It's my own practice that I need to relax into the here and now a bit more. We pick this career because it's how we want to live our lives, so we really do need to be practicing that off the mat in all aspects.

best advice:

Do a bit of research and find a catchment area
that isn't already served by regular teachers.
This is both to give your own business
a chance to flourish, but also to practice
respectful ethics towards other teachers, which
needs to be the foundation of what you do.

Charlotte Watts UK

SHOOTING YOGA

Someone once described to me the business opportunity presented by the internet as akin to the Wild West when gold prospectors risked it all to strike it rich.

It's a great comparison. Not in that you're taking your life in your hands; more, the unpredictable nature of where the online world is heading.

Fortune favours the brave so if you have creative flair, a bit of talent, and a plan, then there's no reason why the internet can't work well for your yoga business too.

Lots of people are already doing it. There are plenty of big name online yoga providers now offering huge amounts of free and paid for content.

Some of it is very high quality. Study what they're doing before starting out in this area, but don't be daunted by it. There are a lot of individual yoga teachers doing their own things successfully and making money from it. Online yoga is extremely cost competitive compared to attending regular real life classes and gives people so much more flexibility as to how and when they practice. No, of course it's not the same as a real class where you can hang out in the juice bar afterwards, but this is the way the world is going. Whatever it is that you're offering - yoga classes, inspiring talks, meditation - video is a great way to get your message across.

banish doubt

HERE ARE A FEW **QUESTIONS** TO ASK YOURSELF BEFORE HITTING THE CAMERA'S **RECORD** BUTTON

WHY? Before you set up your camera think about why you're doing this. Don't just throw some shapes on the mat, and hope for the best. What's the driving purpose? Think about it as a way of empowering people, to help them heal, or to transform lives. Your online video could be changing people's lives for the better.

WHO? Typically, that's you (the movie star) although if you are really camera shy there's no harm inviting a guest teacher to be in your production. Be engaging and don't freak out if you've never seen yourself on screen before. Although you can do it all yourself, getting others involved - cameraman (or woman), video editor, or some tech geeks - will boost professionalism.

WHAT? What exactly do you want to share? When you're ready to film, make sure you have a clear plan as to what you want to say before the camera starts rolling. Any sequence should have a clear purpose for viewers.

Think and plan ahead, then jot down a script and get ready for rehearsals. This ain't Hollywood but you can at least pretend for a little.

WHEN? It takes just a few seconds to upload content online. However, make sure your video is exactly as you want it before pressing the 'send' button. That means the more time you put into it the better the final product. Don't rush as this will be an advertisement for your business.

WHERE? Think about location. If you've got space at home then use that. Lighting is crucial so check your filming is coming out as you'd like it. The natural world is great for filming yoga but bear in mind the weather, which will influence lighting.

HOW? Consult others about the best equipment to use. Some use an iPhone to record short sequences but if you're after longer videos then you may need a better camera. Start small, see how it goes, then work your way up.

Kellie Adkins (USA)

HOLISTIC BUSINESS AND MARKETING MENTOR AND CERTIFIED YOGA THERAPIST

KELLIE ADKINS STARTED ONLINE VIDEO WORK AFTER CLOSING HER YOGA STUDIO

I was drawn to yoga at an early age
I struggled through childhood and young adulthood with body shame, disordered eating and depression. I found yoga because nothing else seemed to fit. I am fascinated by the human form and the overlaps between the body, mind and spirit. This truly informs everything I do as a business coach and yoga educator.

Video is a steep learning curve
I stepped into the online yoga and content world after closing my bricks and mortar yoga studio. The biggest challenge I faced can be summed up in two words: learning curve. This is steep for the online content world.

I brought in third party help
I hired a mentor with specific experience in online marketing and content strategy that helped immensely. I still had to figure out the technical side of things and learn the tools of the trade and that took time.
Combine your teaching with other work. Diversifying your revenue streams always helps, especially when you are just getting started as a teacher. If you have a full or part-time job that provides additional benefits, keep that going until your passion project takes off.

I've continued to build two businesses | My coaching practice and my integrative yoga education institute:

they each feed my soul. If you're doing work that feeds you (energetically or financially) keep that up while you dip your toe in the yoga water.

TOP 3 TIPS FOR DABBLING IN VIDEO FOR THE FIRST TIME:

DO have a plan
Map out what you want to say, how you're going to say it and why it's important for the viewer. Better yet, have a clear, specific content strategy and a blow-by-blow of your videos. I separate strategy days from filming days and even have all my clothing ready to swap out from video to video.

DO speak directly to your ideal viewer (your dream client)
You can speak to anyone but you can't speak to everyone. Know who you are talking to and what problem your video/tip/service solves. Not everyone needs to start by offering foundational and therapeutic yoga sequence video shorts (like I did). If you're catering to a population of experienced yogis, you may begin by offering asana tips and tools for stronger practice.

DON'T forget to consider camera angles for filming yoga
Filming yoga shots is different than speaking directly to the camera. You may need 2-3 filming perspectives for a single video. Consider what your audience needs to see.

Best advice:

If you're just starting out, you'll save hundreds of hours of time and (potentially) thousands of dollars by investing in the right support. Making the transition online can be very discouraging (and costly) at first, especially if you are not 'techie'. Find someone with experience in the online yoga world and seek out a business buddy for encouragement.

Making movies

THINK ABOUT WHAT YOU'RE TRYING TO **ACHIEVE** FIRST BEFORE YOU PICK UP THE **CAMERA**

In our digital age, video content is very engaging; as much as 90% of our communication is non-verbal. And, with the internet in virtually every home and on every smartphone, it represents an opportunity not to be missed, whatever your line of work. It's the next best thing if you can't do face-to-face yoga in real life.

1 Online work and videos can be a great way to fill a gap in your community. If you know who your audience is you'll be delivering a great and much-needed service to them. It means they can keep in touch with you when they're not at class, and maybe need some extra support at home.

2 It can be incredibly simple and cheap to start out, although highly professional content is likely to involve superior equipment and come at a cost. For newbies, start with your iPhone. It's the perfect way to get a feel for what it's all about. If you're posting to YouTube, then use it to film horizontally (not vertical), as it works better.

3 There are so many platforms to promote your work to others as well, from YouTube and Google+ to Skype. Explore them all.

4 Before you even set up your camera ask yourself what is the driving purpose behind everything you share (for example, empowering others to heal, or transform)?

5 Know beforehand what you are going to share and who it is you are targeting with your work. This will help you tailor your content to their needs. You can talk to anyone but you can't talk to everyone. Find your tribe.

6 Like social media, video work is not for everyone. Some people fear how they'll be perceived on camera, or don't like the sound of their own voice. The truth is not everyone is a natural performer. Get some training if you want it, otherwise, don't sweat it.

7 Check out the multitude of video packages, platforms and editing software out there that might be useful, many for free (Skype, Wello, Popexpert, Udemy, iMovie), but don't be daunted by it. You don't need all of it. And if it's totally baffling, then get help.

Notes from the director's chair

SIMPLE STEPS TO MAKING **VIDEO** WORK FOR YOU

How long your video lasts depends on what it's for. For a very brief promo then 1-3 minutes is all you need. Save the hour-long recordings until you get some experience under your belt; you'll need professional equipment and assistance to make high quality longer videos.

Content ideas are limitless. Show off your fabulous asana. If your Cobra's great then run through that step-by-step. Give your video series a cool name, like Awesome Asanas: 7 poses (one a week) to elevate your yoga practice.

As always, connect and share your video content through all of your networks to maximise exposure. More marketing stuff, I'm afraid.

And, while we're on the marketing theme, make a splash out of it all. Don't be shy, you're doing this to help people and get your videos seen by as many people as possible. Create a buzz. Set up a 'virtual retreat': 21 days of online content sent to people (combining asana, meditation, nutrition) via email, and hosted on your website or on YouTube.

Find someone else to record and edit your video if possible, although it can be costly to hire professionals. Get a friend who'll help for free if you can.

Every video must answer a series of inter-related questions, so have a plan before you press the record button.

If possible, use a microphone, particularly if you are going to be talking through the sequence as you are doing it. It's usually better to record the sequence first, then record your voice after that.

Choose a nice location: if the weather's good then a pretty, natural spot outside is perfect. If that's not an option then find an attractive space indoors. If you're home is too cramped or messy then find another venue, maybe at a friend's house.

If you are doing a 'how to' video then you will probably benefit from having a simple script. The viewer definitely doesn't want to watch you reading from your notes on the floor, however.

If you are speaking direct to the camera then consider what the backdrop is. You don't want people distracted by what's going on behind you.

Start with some free content, posted on YouTube or your website, but make sure it includes something of value to your potential viewer target market.

Once you've got that ticked off, build interest to a point where you can pay for better production. This will be a step up the ladder of professionalism.

Just start creating: people will tell you if your video sucks. And if it does, have a re-think, get some help if you need it, and try, try again.

YOGA ROCKSTAR TIP #16

'SHARE FROM THE HEART'

"If you keep sharing from your heart, and from what you know, you will slowly attract people who resonate with what you have to share"

Nikki Ralston | New Zealand

Developing your own TT course

TRAINING THE YOGA TEACHERS OF THE FUTURE

When you first start out, it's inconceivable that one day you might be the person training up the yoga teachers of the future. But why not? Once you've got the experience, you're as good as anyone else. And you're different. You've got a unique set of skills and talents to bring to the table.

This is proper advanced yoga now, so you'll need to know your stuff before embarking on this route. As a rule, you'll probably need to have your 500 hour qualifications before you can start thinking about this.

There's a good starter point though in assisting other lead trainers on their courses. They may be good, but even the world's top instructors can't do it all alone. Similarly, if there's a yoga teacher training group of up to 50 people then there's no way one person can be in charge without any assistance; that's a great way to cut your teeth and transfer some of your skills and experiences to the new, upcoming yoga teachers of the future.

If you're ambitious, or you feel that it's time for something new, then maybe you're ready to go about creating you're very own teacher training programe. It's a grueling process, but there's help and support available, and - as many instructors in this book will tell you - it can most definitely be done.

Call for assistace

ASSISTING ANOTHER LEAD **TRAINER** WILL HELP YOU **LEARN** THE ROPES

Really, this is just about notching it up a level. But you've got to be at the top of your game, as you'll be working with some advanced practitioners.

The job is slightly different to teaching regular students, but there are obvious similarities. Remember, it's your task to impart knowledge on the class that you're working with; your new 'students' need to learn something from their contact time with you. After all, you're teaching them now so that they can teach in the future; it's not a time for you to show off your own practice or many years of wisdom.

It also helps if you have a niche here too, an area where you have perhaps a greater level of expertise or personal interest, such as class planning, posture work, anatomy and physiology, yoga philosophy, or the history of yoga.

One of the good things about becoming a more experienced yoga teacher - and potentially assisting on other teacher training courses - is that you'll most likely qualify for higher pay grades. This is a natural progression given your pedigree.

With that additional experience, it means you'll probably pocket more money at studios where you work too. Everywhere is different, of course, but that's certainly true in places where teacher fees are on a sliding scale according to experience and qualifications.

Ultimately, all of this builds your experience and understanding, so that if you do choose to develop your own teaching course, you are better equipped to do so.

throw some glitter

Get Inspired

JILL LAWSON SET UP HER OWN TEACHER TRAINING COURSE AFTER SEEING CLASS NUMBERS SWELL AT HER STUDIO IN SOUTH-WEST COLORADO

Teacher training was a natural progression | As the interest in yoga kept growing in my area, so did the need for more classes. Certifying yoga teachers seemed like the next logical step for me.

Keep up the standards | Yoga Alliance requires minimum standards for yoga schools to be accepted as part of their accreditation programme. I developed my lesson plans based on these standards, leaving room to expound a bit more deeply into anatomy and physiology, as those are my areas of expertise. Having a graduate degree in exercise science, plus experience teaching college, gave me the tools to create a solid course outline.

Face your fears | At times, I wondered how I could possibly know anything about a 5,000-year-old discipline from a part of the world I'd never

visited. I had to face my fears, take a humble approach, and pay attention to the lessons I would also be learning throughout the course. Now, every course I teach reminds me that I am human, and that learning is an ongoing process, especially for teachers.

Be ready for anything | Be prepared, but leave room for your course to unfold organically. Breakthroughs and life- transformations may take place in your students, and it is wise to hold space for that to happen. Set your lesson plan aside and be open to the moment. Listen to your students and encourage them to contribute their own perspectives on yoga.

Love your students | Most importantly, inspire your students to be themselves. Watching them blossom into wonderful yoga teachers is worth its weight in gold.

best advice:
Build a strong curriculum and follow through with it. If you don't understand something, learn it. Seek out experts who can help teach and share their knowledge with your students.

Jill Lawson USA

The devil is in the detail

IF YOU WANT TO **CREATE** YOUR OWN TEACHER TRAINING COURSE, THEN YOU'RE EMBARKING ON A POTENTIALLY **LUCRATIVE,** BUT HIGHLY COMPETITIVE, YOGA FIELD

People go on to create their own teacher training courses for a whole bunch of reasons. Often, it's a natural progression after a long career teaching and running successful retreats and workshops. For big yoga stars then it's an obvious way to reach out to more people and extend their community. Others want to create a course that is more closely aligned with their own beliefs, style, or personality. These are all valid reasons.

Whatever your motivations, it's not something to be entered into lightly. Starting up any new yoga course requires enormous intellectual input and a fair bit of outlay. Once again, this means a lot of research and planning before you can even get down to the real work. You'll first need to identify precisely why you want to run your own teacher training school, and what you'll be providing over and above what others are offering. There are thousands of options out there: what makes your course idea so different?

You'll need to devise and structure your course so that it meets all the requirements of the big yoga accreditation bodies too; this way, they can support you and work with you as you get started. This is vital if you want your course to be credible and accepted across the industry, at home and potentially overseas as well.

BEFORE YOU START

Course content: you've got to know precisely what you're going to include in your course. If you don't know, then how will your students know? Again, be crystal clear why you're doing this - this will guide your course planning and ultimately help to shape your content.

Resources: your teacher training resources might include manuals, DVDs and many other things. All of these take time to prepare and must be done to very high standards. If they're not, you're students will see through it.

Manuals: writing a teacher training manual is not for the faint hearted. This could be 100 page (or more) document, but it forms a vital part of the course content. I've seen lots of these things and some are magical, inspiring reads, while others are plain dull. If you want to shine above the rest, then you've got to put the time in. If you can't write very well, then get someone to help you on this one

MARKETING

Promotion: with competition intense, you've got to be spot on when it comes to selling your course idea and values. The more passionate about it you are, the more you'll be able to convey this in your marketing. Get that message across: tell students what they need to know; why they've got to sign up. Make it easy for them to decide.

Community: your pool of students is pretty much limitless here, so think big, although clearly any marketing will need to be tailored and specific to where you think your core target market is. Obviously, the higher your profile and reach before starting out, the easier the marketing task will be.

Commissions: the best referral is always word of mouth. Give commission to your graduates who get new people to sign up. That's a great way to do business.

THE BOTTOM LINE

Cost: as in planning retreats and other ventures, you'll need to do a lot of number crunching here. The principles are the same, however: keep a close eye on your costs to know where your break even point is, and then work up from there. This will help you work out how much to charge your potential students as well. The cost of attending a yoga teacher training can run into thousands; it's a serious investment. That means you've got to get your figures right when planning.

Practical details: where will you hold your course; how long will it be; will you require help from other teachers or assistants? You won't know your costs until you answer these (and many other) questions.

Sales: your teacher training course essentially becomes a new business within your mini yoga empire.

As such, it needs to be treated like any other business. This means marketing, selling, and ultimately, getting people to sign up for your offer. Not everyone will be able to pay upfront, so do what you can to make it affordable for all.

OTHER CONSIDERATIONS

The wow factor: you don't need gimmicks to run a successful course (avoid them, in fact), but there's nothing stopping you delivering some real magic to students (no, I don't mean pulling a rabbit out of a hat). Students will remember the lavish, fun, healthy banquets and chitchat at the end of the day, especially if you're there to talk shop with them.

The personal touch: some teachers assign much of their course duties to assistants. You're perfectly entitled to do this, but students love actual contact with the personality or leader behind it all. Make yourself available for your students.

Labour of love: be aware of the impact you may be having on people; your course could mark a life-defining transition for a student. Be sensitive to their needs. If you love that idea and want to help them in their transformative journey then you're most definitely in the right business.

Business support: give your students a helping hand as they transition into the world of paid teaching work. This might simply be a small module inside the training course, or some information in the manual. Some teachers offer ongoing support, or create an online community, to assist teachers as they start out. One studio chain in London (Fierce Grace) offers newbie teachers a budget studio to learn their trade, where classes are cheaper for students. It's a nice touch. Not all students will want this support but it's nice to know it's there if they do.

How I made it happen

BE CONFIDENT IN YOUR WORTH, AND IN YOUR CRAFT, SAYS ANA FORREST

Ana Forrest USA

Leave your stuff at the door | Be present for your students. Strong quality of attention and passion to learn are essential to becoming a great teacher.

Breathe deeply when teaching | Punctuate your cues with silences, giving your students the time to follow your directions. Practice your sequence, giving it a 'road test' before teaching it. Make sure it works physiologically. Do some yoga before teaching so that it's alive in your blood and you're warmed up and safe to demo. Now you can teach from a truly authentic place. Connect to your love of yoga and your desire to help people as you teach.

Take different teaching opportunities | Take as many different teaching opportunities as possible, with as many different kinds of people, to get versatile and flexible in your problem-solving with your students.

Don't give up the day job | I recommend, at least for the first year, maybe two years, to keep your regular paying job as well as teach. This gives your baby yoga teacher some time to get seasoned and grow up. It's an unnecessary hardship to put all of your living expenses on this newly burgeoning teacher. It's easy to suffocate inspiration by giving the young yoga teacher too much financial responsibility too fast.

Have business ethics that make you proud | With regards to money: be as impeccable with your money flow as you are with flows of energy through your body and in your class. It's not wrong to make a profit out of teaching yoga.

do more yoga

It's important to be honest | Be willing to say, 'I don't know, let's find out what works'. The fact is, you studied to teach. More than likely your student did not. You have something of great value for them. Stand in the truth of your worth. Teach with confidence in your craft.

What's your personal mantra | Evolve or Die

best advice:

Most importantly, do a daily yoga practice that builds your passion. Keep your commitments to yourself and your profession. Make a part of your intent to learn something new each day. Definitely cultivate and grow your love – love needs tending.

#9

Sensational Studios

breathe deeply

"I'm not going to change
the way i look or the way
i feel to conform to anything.
I've always been a freak"

John Lennon

be fearless

*"Go confidently
in the direction of
your dreams"*

Henry David Thoreau

dream big

A space of your own

OPENING A YOGA STUDIO IS AN **ACHIEVABLE DREAM.** BUT DON'T UNDERESTIMATE THE CHALLENGE

Opening your own studio is a dream for many yogis, but not all. Though it scores high in the glamour stakes - a gorgeous space to call your own, a place to offer your unique blend of yoga to the world - it also ranks as one of the most stressful (and costly) ventures to pursue.

Money can be tight. Some studios are big but others are operating by the seat of their pants. Don't be put off by this, however, if this is genuinely your dream. Some studios do make their owners good money.

If you're someone that enjoys the ride, and will respond in a positive way to all the challenges and stresses that a yoga studio throws up (and there are many) then this might be for you.

On the other hand, if you're going to be worried sick at project managing the minutest of details, fretting over falling customer numbers, or stalling sales, then it might be best avoided.

You need to go into this with eyes wide open to reduce the possibility of failure. Managing your money is crucial in a project of this scale: opening a studio will entail investment, and probably lots of it, depending on what your plans are and where you're located.

But it can be done. Just look for examples of beautiful and successful studios near to you. No studio owner will tell you it's easy (it really isn't), but if you do things right, then it can be well worth the effort and an amazing experience for all involved.

Where to begin

NOW LET'S TURN THOSE **DREAMS** INTO **REALITY**

Start with the basics. It helps if you have a clear vision of what you want. For instance, whether you just want a space for yoga classes, or if you want to make it more of a holistic wellness centre, to include treatment and therapy rooms, or other activities, even a cafe. Much of this might be determined by cost - your budget might limit some of these options - so it pays to think ahead. This is where you can give your dreams clarity, before the actual business planning and number crunching starts.

When it comes to detailed planning, the list is practically endless: locating a property, studio design and building work, through to class scheduling, teacher recruitment, marketing activities and promotion.

Also, keep in mind that opening your yoga studio is really just the beginning. Making it profitable and successful long-term is the real challenge. And that will require a lot of hands-on management, some careful nurturing, and attention to detail, day-by-day. Like opening any small business it can feel pretty grueling at times.

Talk to studio owners and find out how they did it. Learn from their experiences and mistakes. If they can do it, you can do it.

life's for living

The good, the bad and the ugly of studio ownership

THE GOOD

For the love of others: creating your own unique yoga space for others to find peace and relaxation is a truly rewarding experience

Making a living: there's no better way to pay the bills than hanging out at your own studio

Nothing beats it: turning your yoga studio dream into a reality is an unbelievable achievement

THE BAD

Be prepared to work your socks off: like any small business, running a yoga studio is hard work

Success takes time: Rome wasn't built in a day. Don't expect the world to race to your opening night party

The boring stuff: you can't inspire people all the time. Sometimes you'll just be cleaning the toilets

THE UGLY

Balancing the books: get a handle on your finances. If you don't, your dream could easily become a nightmare

Competitive instincts: not everyone will share your vision, from other studio owners to teachers you might employ. It's not very yogic, but be prepared for some rivalries

Stay strong: be prepared for some dark days even if you are ultimately successful. You will face setbacks at some point

YOGA ROCKSTAR TIP #17

'MAKING A LIVING'

"I taught classes for free for years until I realised this created an imbalance in the exchange of energy. As a new teacher, I wish I'd known that marketing can be ethical and that receiving a fair wage for an honest day's work is okay."

Cheryl MacDonald | UK

Community Relations

NURTURING THE COMMUNITY IS AN INTEGRAL PART OF ANY SUCCESSFUL YOGA STUDIO

Essentially, you're starting a new business here. But there's a mighty difference too. You're not just selling IT components or bread, you're building a community, you're looking to transform the lives of others.

Many people don't just want to come in for an hour and a stretch on the mat, they want to be involved, to feel a part of something bigger.

So keep this in mind when you start planning. Make your studio a communal experience. This is what I personally want from my time at a yoga studio. I can get my yoga anywhere. What I want is to feel a part of the family. So make it a team experience, for students and staff alike.

Appreciate the diversity of your community (including kids and seniors); build it from the ground up. Help and heal others and all will benefit (including you). Watch people blossom and grow as your studio evolves. If you can do that then you're onto a winner.

Let money be no part of your equation for wanting to open a studio. Yes, you've got to keep a keen eye on the financials, but an accountant or anyone else can do that; it's not the only thing that will determine your long-term success.

Get Inspired

LOUISE PALMER-MASTERTON TELLS THE STORY OF HOW POPULAR CAMBRIDGE YOGA STUDIO, CAMYOGA, WAS BORN

A beautiful yoga space was always in the back of my mind from when I first started practicing Ashtanga; an urban sanctuary for *satsang*, as a friend describes our studios now. When I first started teaching under the Camyoga name, I had a lot of people coming together to share their practice with me, so it felt like I was being propelled towards this outcome right from the start.

The beginning: when I first viewed some premises, and I ran the figures, it looked pretty scary so I put it to one side. The real search began some years later when my business was more secure and we had a good client base. I looked to others for professional help finding premises in the beginning, but it wasn't until I took control and did things myself that the project began to unfold.

The search: I viewed a lot of spaces. It's like buying a house, you just know when you walk in if a place is right for you, and almost all were not. Most 'good' places in Cambridge are hotly contested, and we were up against established blue chip companies so got turned down a few times. But I roll with serendipity, and now, of course, looking back, thank goodness we did not get those other spaces as the perfect one was just around the corner.

The location: as soon as I walked in to what would become our first studio I knew I could make it work. It was the perfect location right in central Cambridge, two open plan floors to give two decent sized studios (25+ mats) and a café in our own detached building. And the owners were real people I could talk to; it was simply having a face-to-face chat that clinched the deal in the end.

Raising money: it may sound simple, but I had this very strong vision of what I wanted, and the money just simply appeared at the right time. I never really doubted that it would, as the whole project felt so right. Camyoga is mainly built from the financial support from friends and family, and if you're able to raise money in this way, then this is by far the best option.

Louise Palmer-Masterton, UK

What I learned along the way

Stay true to your own passion and vision and everything will work out just fine. Trust yourself and your own instincts, even if it's not your current area of expertise. Have the courage and energy to keep pursuing your goal. Keep an open mind as to the type of space that might work, and remember, a good location will cost you more, but is worth it as the footfall will be far greater. It's all about vision. Stay strong to your vision and the rest will fall into place. Oh, and don't believe that life is too short: life is long, and within one life you can have many lives. Above all, do what you want to do, not what someone else wants you to do.

Moving in: I did all the design and dealt with the contractors myself. I spent hours doing drawings and looking at possibilities to get the maximum out of the space. Looking back it was probably this process that put so much life into the spaces.

Second studio: our first studio got very busy very quickly, so less than a year in I started to consider a second location. Managing our busy training school in the space alongside our classes programme had become a challenge. So the new location would be to house the training school, and give us a bigger studio to hold workshops and events for 50+ people. We had a different set of requirements for this studio: a bigger studio, car parking and a bigger café/breakout space being important.

What next: people say the atmosphere at Camyoga is tangible. You can feel an energy shift as soon as you walk through the door. We have managed to replicate that for our second studio, and for me that was very important. More studios? Watch this space.

The right location

CHOOSE THE RIGHT SPACE IF YOU WANT TO MAXIMISE YOUR CHANCES OF SUCCESS

Don't rush this bit. When you know you want to proceed, then finding the right space and location is all important in determining long-term success.

There's no single formula for this, however, so the perfect spot may to some extent hinge on your business plans. For instance, if you want a lot of footfall to pull passers by through the doors then you'll need a central location in the town where there are plenty of people about. If you're planning to concentrate on workshops or teacher training then this may be less important. Here are a few other things you might want to ponder:

Location: this is probably the single most important decision you'll make. Bite the bullet and go where your people are. A big space in an out-of-town industrial park may be cheaper, but a central location will generate far more traffic.

Access: parking is important but not a deal-breaker. If you're in the town centre then there should be alternative parking options anyway. Do some research and find out how your people will travel to their yoga class.

Studio size: small is cheaper, of course, but you need a space thats large enough for you to make some money. Typically, that's enough room for about 25+ mats. If you can only fit in 12 mats, then that's going to seriously limit how much you can make from classes. Having said that I also know of (profitable) studios with space for just four (yes, four!) mats.

Cafe: even a small cafe or hangout area can make all the difference to the user experience. It doesn't have to be complicated: just offer tea and a few snacks. Invite people to come before their class, and stay afterwards, this is what people will buy into and keep them coming back for more.

3 secrets to studio success

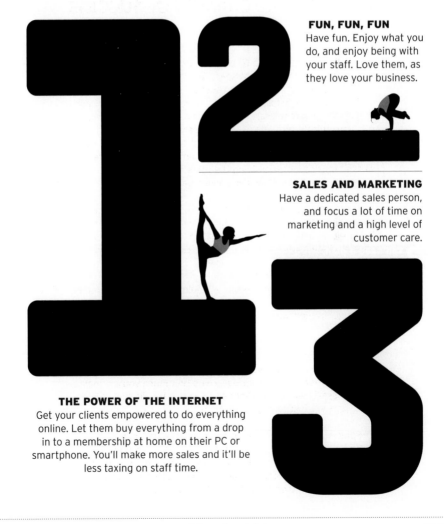

FUN, FUN, FUN
Have fun. Enjoy what you do, and enjoy being with your staff. Love them, as they love your business.

SALES AND MARKETING
Have a dedicated sales person, and focus a lot of time on marketing and a high level of customer care.

THE POWER OF THE INTERNET
Get your clients empowered to do everything online. Let them buy everything from a drop in to a membership at home on their PC or smartphone. You'll make more sales and it'll be less taxing on staff time.

Debbie Lynn

10 THINGS YOU SHOULD KNOW ABOUT OPENING A YOGA STUDIO

1 It is a business: don't give it away. Although yoga is a spiritual endeavour, giving free classes is a quick way to financial ruin. While that is a noble gesture, 'free' will not pay the bills. This is simply reality and unless you have the funds to teach for free you will end up closing faster than you opened.

2 Friends, family and entitlement: discount? Perhaps, but respectfully. If someone feels they are entitled to receive freebies then handle them with care. They are the souls who can and will suck you dry if you allow it to happen.

3 You need a plan. While flow is a wonderful quality, you need a real business plan and you must be brutally honest about your capabilities to maintain it. Forecasting up to five years is a good place to start. If you don't know about or know how to create a business plan, get educated. There's an abundance of information online. No excuses. It will be a guide for you as you travel through being a small business owner. (The wise will tell you it is imperative.)

4 You'll have real expenses. There are multiple costs associated with a successful studio: taxes, overheads, advertising and marketing, payroll (yourself included), cleaning, insurance and on and on. This is the one place that is hard for the 'yogi' mind. Keep up-to- date on your books and wrap your head around costs and analysis. I understand there is nothing more 'corporate' than accounting, but do it; please do it. A few minutes of savvy bookkeeping will save you a lot of time and trouble in the long run.

5 Stay out of the 'guru' syndrome. Taking on drama will deplete you. Keep business and personal issues separated. It is not your job to fix, counsel, or repair anyone's broken anything. It is your job and duty to teach and give love, not personal advice. There is a big difference.

6 It's hard work. Be prepared to sink every penny, every waking moment, and all your energy into honing in on, perfecting, and enhancing your classes. There will be ups and downs. This is life so be pro-active about it. Use committed action (your own practice) and patience. It will serve you well and in the end form a solid ground for inner success that extends outward.

7 Spread the word. Community evolvement is a brilliant way to get known. Word of mouth via helping the community is good for the soul, good for what ails you, and good for all relationships. Period. 'Pay it back' works; it is the karmic wheel, that is

wake up happy

a basis for manifestation. Energy in, energy out. Action creates action. Satisfaction and peace is a gift of community outreach.

8 **Keep your speeches and personal opinions short and sweet.** Not everyone will align with your ideas. It is important to know who you are teaching, (remember, yoga has crossed over into the mainstream).

9 **When you are ready to hire, do your homework.** Follow up on referrals, past work experiences, and personally attend the prospect's class.

Make sure their agenda is in alliance with yours and that they understand they are working for the studio (for you) and it isn't a competition.

10 **Take expansion slowly.** If you have grown quickly, be wary, be careful. Just be. There is the huge temptation to become a bigger studio, hire new instructors, expand, but this is a very tricky space to be in. Make sure you don't get in too deep. Again, run the numbers. Time and money - your time and money - is on the line. Expanding too fast (as with anything) will hurt and can take you down fast.

YOGA ROCKSTAR TIP #18

'MONEY MATTERS'

"Be as impeccable with your money flow as you are with flows of energy through your body and in your class. It's not wrong to make a profit out of teaching yoga."

Ana Forrest | USA

believe in magic

Balancing act

FINDING THE **BALANCE** BETWEEN INCOME GENERATION AND MAKING YOGA ACCESSIBLE TO ALL

This is your livelihood so you'll need your studio to bring in income all year round, and enough to cover both your own needs and to pay your staff.

Right from the start, you've got to build in the potential for revenue generation, both from classes as well as other products (like workshops). This means you'll need lots of classes (mornings, days, evenings), so there's nearly always something going on. This is great for building community too.

If you have an existing client base then you have a great springboard for launching a studio. It's not a pre-requisite but it helps.

Pricing your classes and workshops right, again, is all part of running a successful studio business. Be careful here though. It's important to offer a pay-as-you-go membership so you're not just a big shot studio signing up people on year-long subscriptions. For me, when I've got extra money I'll pay for a subscription, but when I'm broke I need the flexibility of the budget option.

Affordability

Make classes affordable. These are hard times. No one should be turned away because of their lack of money. Just seeing the sign 'all welcome' or 'free yoga' outside makes me feel good. Sadly, in my own experience, this is something most studios fail at. They are - quite rightly - geared up to getting paying students through the doors. If they don't do this, they will fail. It's pretty easy to bag a free class here and there, but do look out for those who really - genuinely - need it. It's hard, but do try and cater for all.

Staying afloat

THE NITTY GRITTY OF **STUDIO** FINANCE

by Louise Palmer-Masteron of Camyoga)

CASH FLOW
This is the biggest challenge for any business. Yoga businesses are no exception. On the one hand, we do receive much of our money in advance; on the other, seasonality means that income is not at the same level each month of the year. January can be great; August can be 'help!'.

Do try and negotiate with all your service providers (rent, rates) to pay everything monthly. This is unusual certainly for rent which is typically paid quarterly, but most landlords will be open to this, particularly if you ask right from the start.

Do work with a merchant account and card processing company who pays you daily and without a high 'rolling reserve' (this means they withhold a percentage of your money, sometimes for up to six months, which can really add up).

Do analyse the profitability of everything: every class, every workshop, and every aspect of the business. Focus on those bits that are more profitable.

Do try not to be dependent on any service provider. Keep your options open, and don't be afraid to change. It's your business; try not to have all your eggs in one basket. If your service providers 'break' you are dependent on these people. Have a contingency in place. Look ahead. Always.

Do hope for the best, but plan for the worst.

TAX, STAFFING COSTS, OVERHEADS
These are high for a yoga studio but will vary enormously depending on where you are. Most studio expenses are manpower. Given that almost no expenses are deductible, a large slice of everything you earn will go to sales tax. Add to that card processing fees and you're really only earning 75% of what you receive.

Do have a separate account and put sales tax money in there for all income received. Do this religiously.

Do challenge your rates and see if you can get a deduction. There

live your dreams

are a number of agencies that will do this for you.

Do research in advance the going rate for staff and teachers to ensure you all get a good deal. It's easy to increase pay but very hard to cut pay. Give your staff perks (such as free membership) that count for a lot but actually cost you nothing financially.

Do shop around for everything: from researching cheaper gas and electric to cheaper studio management software and merchant accounts.

SEASONALITY

SEASONALITY I recall our first Christmas. It was two months after we'd opened, and compared to the fantastic busy-ness of the first two months, it was like the Mary Celeste. I panicked. Of course, it was short lived and we were back to happier days in January, but it's wise to plan for this. Over time, the business has become less susceptible to any kind of fluctuation.

Do be creative and offer additional purchase items at traditionally quieter times such as Christmas gifts and other retail items - plan ahead for this and get stocked up in November.

Do fill your studios with other activities in the summer - things like residential trainings during July and August.

Do focus your marketing ahead of time (in December generate sales for January, in August generate sales for September). Do this via hard-to-resist special offers.

Do focus your marketing on educating your clients that yoga is a year round activity. Put on special fun classes during traditionally quieter times.

Do reduce your offerings if your studio gets quieter: do not delay in doing this. Your clients may moan a little but you can bring the classes back later. Keep clients well informed.

Do believe that as your business grows and numbers increase overall, you will be less susceptible to seasonality.

Do try not to be a self fulfilling prophecy 'if you believe your business will be quiet in August, then it probably will be'. Get creative rather than succumb to this mindset.

"Cash flow, managing costs, and the seasonal nature of yoga studios, are all part of the challenge"

Re-selling

THINK ABOUT RE-SELLING OTHER PRODUCTS AS A SEPARATE INCOME STREAM

As their yoga instructor, you are an inspiration to your clients (at least let's hope so). That means when you stroll in with some cool new kit, or a snugly blanket around your shoulders, they may well be interested in emulating you.

If you have a studio (even if you don't) then re-selling products is a great way to make a little extra money. Don't expect too much but it could provide an added boost to your business.

Find out first what your people like and what they might be interested in buying (yoga books, DVDs, mats, cushions, blocks). Clothing requires a little more research (sizes, colours) but show students pictures first to gauge their level of interest. Don't just expect them to buy what you like.

In the studio, set aside a small space to present things beautifully. All products need to be well presented if people are going to want to buy them. Don't just hide things away in a dusty corner.

If you're just a solo teacher, or studio space is super tight, then you can still load up products on your website for folks to buy. Host a product party to show things to your students. You must make a bit of effort (marketing, again!) otherwise no one will know about your items for sale. Don't bombard them, just use your social networks; re-blog product reviews from other sites; show them nice images.

Don't be shy approaching any companies with a view to selling their products; they want to sell their stuff, after all. An ambassador relationship may work if you want to cut any risk, where you pocket a commission for any recommendation that leads to a sale with your sponsor company.

Ever wanted to work in publishing?

A lot of studios sell OM magazine on a no risk basis. How? Well, the publishers take care of all the transport costs, and all the studio does is request how many copies it wants. They make £1 for every copy they sell, with the balance of the cover price going back to the publisher. If copies are not sold, they are returned to OM HQ (at the publisher's expense). Financially, there's zero risk; it just requires a bit of paperwork and planning and posting (that's honestly not a sales pitch for the mag, I'm just letting you know!).

celebrate victories

Get inspired

NOT CONTENT WITH HER OWN YOGA STUDIO, JO DE ROSA MANIFESTED A STUNNING RETREAT CENTRE

Create a vision board | A retreat centre had been on my vision board for years. I had an ariel shot of a big house with extensive grounds and knew in my heart this was my ultimate dream. For me, once you know what your dream is - and it feels right and exciting - then you can generate the belief that it is actually possible.

Be specific, but be flexible | I didn't want to have a certain picture in my mind of the actual house my retreat centre would operate from. Instead, it was the intention I focused on: the intention to help others find their way to happiness and health through yoga.

Believe in yourself | Picture running a retreat centre. Practice by running retreat weekends/weeks for your students. If you don't believe it can actually happen, then it probably won't. So you have to be mentally committed to your goal.

Be prepared to work hard | You need tons of teaching and retreat experience. I've been a full time yoga teacher for over 15 years now, and I've been through so much in my life (abusive relationship; bankruptcy; endless addictions). It's hard work setting up any new business, let alone one on this scale.

Set yourself up for success | In the years before, I got busy filling and teaching classes, hosting and teaching at countless detox and yoga weekends and weeks, and deepening my own practice.

Surround yourself with inspirational people | Spend less time with people that drain your energy. This can be hard as some of these people may be lifelong friends. But perhaps it's now time to raise your energy and hang out with supportive people who believe in you and your dreams.

Network, network, network | Build your tribe through your website, newsletter, Facebook, and any other networking groups and meetings. I'm also a member of a number of online business groups for entrepreneurs, which have opened up many opportunities and collaborative relationships.

Jo De Rosa UK

The simple things

SOMETIMES THE **SIMPLE** THINGS CAN MAKE ALL THE DIFFERENCE TO A **SUCCESSFUL** STUDIO

As a general rule, studios are great if you love running a business and don't faint at the prospect of doing some paperwork. There are plenty of hard-hitting challenges to face: from hiring and firing people to settling the tax bill. But there are so many other considerations too. Here are a few of the often mundane things that you can expect.

Recruitment: when it comes to recruitment, what sort of people are you looking for? It helps if you all share some core values. It's usually far easier working with teachers that are grounded; these are the ones that will help you build your business long term, not the superstars. You'll also be dealing with subs too.

Teaching: will you want to teach in your own studio or get others in? Probably a mix of both. If you teach, it'll keep your skills fresh, but it'll add more hours to your working week. Of course, one of the great benefits of owning a studio is that you can go to all the classes for free (but that's a very expensive way to get free yoga).

Studio vibe: you're creating a community space here, not just a place to do yoga. Create a nurturing, uplifting environment that clients will want to pay for to repeatedly visit, ideally a few times each week. Make it a place where people will also want to work or just hang out.

Diversification: high rents (and rent increases), lease renewals, local authority taxes; it's a lot for any low margin class-sized business to handle. So you need other things to make it profitable (workshops, teacher training, retail). Respond to new trends or customer demands. By all means be true to yourself but also be open to new things, even if they're not your cup of tea personally.

Sales & marketing: this is a full-time job in itself, so get some help if you can. To get people to pay for your studio you will need endless new clients (it helps here if you're in a good, central location), which typically means lots and lots of marketing. Once you've got them, then you need to retain those clients; this is where your sales charm and interpersonal skills come in.

Vision: it's your own vision - the one that wanted to create the studio in the first place - that will underpin your ultimate success. So stick to your guns

stay true

and have faith in your ideas. Above all, stay in love with yoga at all times. This is a big challenge when there's so much to do, bills to be paid, and so many other things going on, but it's an essential part of any yoga success story.

Competitors: studios should be linked together much more than they are. Anyone who shares your purpose is not a competitor. Any studio near you is a friend. Yes, really. This is important to remember, and to actually believe. If you can, align yourself with them. This may be easier said than done. For example, a multi studio subscription for the area is a great idea on paper, and brilliant for customers, but hard to negotiate and to make workable. Worth exploring though.

Health clubs: regular gyms arguably pose a much greater competitive threat to your studio (and to other local yoga studios, which is why it's great to connect if you can). The big gym might be able to offer so much more for the money (swimming pool, jacuzzi), so offer something else. People desperately want connection, so give them that. Be the place where people want to come to see their friends, to feel welcome, to chat. If you can build real community, and do it more

effectively than the local gym, then you're doing well.

Know your community: know the limits to your studio community. If your local community isn't ready yet for kirtan, don't run a kirtan class just because you fancy it.

Get togethers: live music days, workshops for all - especially those that are admission free - are great for building links within the wider community, and within the studio. Even a summer get together once a year is better than nothing.

Workload: don't underestimate the work you'll be taking on. In the beginning, it can quite literally mean cleaning the toilets and changing the loo roll, as much as running exciting classes for your students. Someone once told me about the value of selling yoga clothing inside a studio; he commented that it was "great, if you like folding t-shirts". What did he mean? For every purchase, you'll get 10 people looking without buying; and all those t- shirts need to be neatly folded away again if they're to be attractive for someone else to buy later on. Guess what? It's you that will be doing all the folding.

"If your local community isn't ready yet for kirtan, don't run a kirtan class just because you fancy it"

The daily grind

WORKING WITH **TEACHERS,** HIRING AND FIRING AND OTHER (NOT ALWAYS) **FUN STUFF**

As an employer, just asking if your people are happy will raise their job satisfaction score. At least you give a damn. Many employers do not. Or if they do, they don't show it.

Of course, a yoga studio is a better place to work than many other alternatives, but it still much depends on the individuals there. There are plenty of things you can do to make your staff happy without paying them any extra.

The starting point for working relationships is usually money, but it doesn't end there. Overall worker satisfaction is likely to be determined not just by pay, but also many other things: that any work is purposeful; colleagues they love: exciting challenges daily; flexibility to work their way; incentives. In the financial sector, it's obviously money and incentives that come first. But that's not why people go into the yoga business.

Just simply ask your staff: what would you like to do? Get them to name their dream work experience, and see if you can help them achieve that. Do they want to teach one class or five classes a week? Do they need a lot of flexibility in how they work? Work with your teachers to help them create their own dream work experience.

Class outlines: these aren't essential, but it can be helpful if you have some guidelines for teachers (especially new ones) to follow on running classes at your studio. Even if you do have them, you can still encourage teachers to be creative and to explore and develop their own sequences.

Meetings: get everyone together for full staff meetings maybe three or four times a year. These should be with a purpose (team building, continuing education), with some sort of takeaway afterwards. Make it attractive to attend: hold a BBQ on the beach if it's summer, or maybe play some music where you can chill together. Sometimes teachers are in the studio so often (for classes) that it's hard to get them to come back for boring meetings. Don't hold a meeting unless there's a genuine purpose. And, if meetings are optional, then send emails instead. Make your staff meetings amazing, not ordinary.

Be mindful of what you share with your staff: it's good to hire

live, laugh, love

"As an employer, just asking if your people are happy will raise their job satisfaction score."

people you like but that doesn't mean having them over every Friday night for wine and gossip. Recognise if you are socialising on a business basis, or on a genuine social basis. Learn the difference if you don't know.

No shows: how often are your teachers allowed to screw up? What about 'no shows'? It's quite a rarity to have a 'no show' teacher and no substitute but it happens. Try and have a back up teacher at the studio, someone to call on in an emergency, maybe a regular at one of your own classes.

Disipline: If you get regular 'no shows' from a teacher, that's a problem. Likewise, if teachers are always calling in their subs (for whatever reason) that's something you also need to address.

Subs: most of the time, teachers are responsible for finding their own subs. However, you want continuity at your studio, so don't go for too many. As for payment, subs typically get paid the same as the teacher. It also helps if the teacher pays the sub for taking their class, rather than go through the studio; it's a messy system otherwise.

Hiring & Firing

No one (except really mean bosses) is ever going to enjoy this part of running a business. But at some point, for whatever reason, it's going to happen. Anything that has an emotional charge to it, such as firing someone, then be sure to do it in person (or on the phone if you have to), but not by text or email. Once you've made your mind up, look at it this way: by not letting a teacher go, you're not allowing them to go out and have the chance to find success elsewhere. One door closes, another door opens. They need the space to let go and to let all that new energy come in for new things and possibilities. I know, it's no fun for anybody here; just be as nice as you can.

How I made it happen

HOT YOGA TRENDSETTER MICHELE PERNETTA OWNS A STRING OF LONDON STUDIOS, BUT STILL RETAINS HER UNIQUE SENSE OF HUMOUR

Michele Pernetta UK

Ingredients for success | You need to be obsessed with other people's health. Being a yoga teacher isn't about your own satisfaction or glory, or about making money. It's about being willing to try anything to help someone heal their knee, or back, or get over their divorce, or cope with their difficult life. You need to be fascinated with the processes yoga awakens in the body and be interested to discuss every single student's back, shoulder, bereavement, little toe, or sprained ankle. And you can't fake it either: you actually have to be a nerd and find nothing more interesting than someone's piles (and how they can sit on their heel in toe-stand if it makes them hurt.)

The yoga business can be tough | People have a misconception that people in the yoga business are enlightened, caring and compassionate people. This isn't the norm. Its brutally competitive and very tribal. On the other hand the yoga practitioners themselves are so inspiring. It's a privilege to meet so many wonderful people. I've had my fair share of business difficulties. But that's the nature of

encourage others

business I suppose. Legal battles, being ripped off, stolen from and blackmailed. Running a business really tests a person on every level.

Things have changed through the years | You used to be able to get away with teaching in a dusty school hall. Now, students expect spotless surroundings, friendly staff, herbal teas and fresh juices. That all comes with a cost, though, so yoga has become more expensive as standards have risen. This creates a slight friction between what we are teaching in yoga, and the need to pay the rent. One has to tread this line carefully.

You get better at dealing with difficulties | I used to get upset when bad things happened, but just like yoga, you gradually build strength and muscle, and can handle more without it taking you off centre. I still go there sometimes but I know what I have to do to get back on track: yoga, meditation and ayurveda are my staples. I also love sewing, painting silk and doing mosaics, and failing that a glass or two of wine and a box set.

10

My Fab Yoga Business

"*The great thing about rock and roll is that someone like me can be a star.*"

Elton John

life is a choice

The best way to predict the future is to create it

you totally rock

Making it big

LOOK TO THE STARS BUT KEEP YOUR FEET ON THE GROUND

If you find yourself, one day in the future, sipping mocktails on a private yacht, scanning the sun-drenched Santa Monica shoreline, take a moment to recount those early years as a newbie instructor.

All the trials and tribulations searching for new students so you can pay the rent, teaching next to a noisy weightlifting class, or that time when one injured student tried to sue you (successfully, as it turned out!).

It'll make for some interesting anecdotes to keep your company of Hollywood A-listers and political power brokers entertained.

In the end, all your dreams came true: hosting fabulous over-subscribed (and spectacularly over-priced) retreats in exotic locations; flown in to accompany Beyonce on her world tour; owning a string of high-end studios in the world's great capital cities; those TV appearances on Oprah.

When your guru urged you to 'think big' on your vision board you certainly delivered.

KEEP IT REAL

Just don't forget the small folk. Keep it real. No matter where fate takes you, no matter how many Arab sheikhs and Russian oligarchs you can count among your friends, there are still new student teachers coming through the ranks. And even more students that turn to yoga for every possible reason imaginable.

Among them all will probably be the next generation of yoga rock stars.

This planet needs them just as much as it does you. So give them a helping hand.

YOGA ROCKSTAR TIP #19

'PUT IN THE HOURS'

"Don't be afraid of hard work. My East Coast work ethic has been my greatest gift in my career. I'm not afraid to put in the hours"

Guru Jagat | *USA*

share your gifts

Join the club

PLOT YOUR WAY THROUGH THE YOGA ROCKSTAR MAZE WITH SOME **ESSENTIAL** KNOWLEDGE

FESTIVALS

Great for exposure and amazing places to be just for the high energy vibe and fantastic like-minded company. Yoga festivals and shows (which now take place all over the world) are a great way to get seen by a lot of people. More festivals are cropping up all the time so plenty of opportunity here.

CELEBRITIES

Yoga's got nothing to do with celebrity culture, right? Correct. However, celebs (as normal human beings) love yoga too, for all the same reasons we do. And someone has to teach them. Why not you? Discretion is required, but it can be a good association for you and an endorsement of your skills.

MEDIA

If you're an established teacher, or you're getting noticed for another reason, then the media will soon want a piece of you. Know how to handle them properly and they'll be your friends for life. They can be brilliant partners for building a career, but highly flammable too if things go wrong.

SPONSORSHIP

If the media love you then sooner or later the corporate world will too. If you're in high demand and have a wide following then expect yoga (and non yoga) brands to come knocking on your door. The bigger this yoga 'industry' gets the more this is going to happen.

Get inspired

PAIGE HELD FOUND HERSELF ON THE COVER OF YOGA JOURNAL, WHICH HAS OPENED UP NEW DOORS IN HER CAREER EVER SINCE

I was lucky to find yoga early on | I'm a native of Fort Lauderdale and found yoga at the age of 16 as my family dynamic was being impacted by my parents' divorce. It sounds like a cliché but I was hooked from that very first class. It became a place where I could resource myself and take care of my physical and mental health.

I love running my own studio | I became a certified teacher in 2000 and later opened my own studio (The Yoga Joint). I'm a mother of two young children and step-mother to two college-age kids. I saw the need for a yoga studio that welcomed families, stressed-out and overwhelmed mums, and decided to offer babysitting twice a day. The studio grew.

The Yoga Journal cover was a dream come true I felt honoured and thrilled to represent my studio, my community, and all working mothers on the cover of a national magazine. My family, friends and students alike were all so excited to see their teacher on the cover. It was a little strange to walk into the supermarket and see myself on the cover among all the other magazines, but it's wonderful to have had that experience.

I manifested the front cover shot | Being on the cover of Yoga Journal was something I manifested. I would walk around town telling people that one day I would be on the cover. Meanwhile, I would live my life, teach and plan my classes, manage my studio, continue to grow and learn, knowing that everything I was doing would move me in the right direction. I knew that one

Paige Held USA

best advice:

Keep up your daily yoga practice asana as well as the other limbs. It's important to stay on your yogic path so you can be the best version of you to help your students find the best version of them.

day all this hard work would create the life that I am now living. Yoga Journal contacted me and six months later I was on the cover.

The cover shot opened doors |

First, that meant being a presenter at one of the Yoga Journal Live conferences. It's a career highlight to be among some of the teachers I've admired for so long, the likes of Seane Corn, Shiva Rea, and Kino MacGregor.

Being a presenter at the conference affords me the opportunity to continue to share my love of yoga and my unique interpretation of the practice (Hot Fusion Flow) with yoga lovers across the country.

I want to open more yoga studios |

I now plan to open more studios in South Florida and I hope to have a stronger presence at future Yoga Journal conferences across the USA.

Get on the circuit

BEFORE YOU CAN **START** THINKING ABOUT APPEARANCES AT ONE OF THE BIG **YOGA** GET-TOGETHERS YOU'VE GOT PAY YOUR DUES

Headlining at places like the amazing Wanderlust festival in the USA or the OM Yoga Show in London (Europe's biggest yoga gathering) doesn't just happen. You've got to spend time in the trenches; you've got to get known before you get booked for a national festival. Again, that means working to build your name and grow your community.

So what do Wanderlust want?

They want you to have popularity already, some public recognition, or expertise in specific areas - and these things don't just happen the day you qualify as a certified instructor. They take time to build and grow.

Don't be invisible: have video; be on YouTube. If you are visible then you will get noticed. It's all part of your strategy, and of course, it doesn't happen overnight.

Be amazing at what you do; mediocre is not good enough. If you are not fabulous then go and take lots more trainings and hang out with extraordinary folks that are. Find that sparkle and then sprinkle some magic of your own.

And, no matter how fabulous you are, keep going to see more teachers because they will always continue to inspire you.

And here's something else to ponder: once you get booked onto the Wanderlust schedule, or you bag that YJ cover shot, make sure you've got something else to 'sell' when folks check you out afterwards (for example, teacher training, Bali retreats, a DVD or a book). Keep it coming: always have new products in the pipeline, whatever they may be. If you don't, then there's nothing new for people to buy. This is how you evolve the brand.

admit mistakes

Reaching out to the media

MEDIA OUTLETS NEED YOU AS MUCH AS YOU NEED THEM. THEY JUST DON'T KNOW IT YET

Getting your voice heard in a noisy world is not always easy but, again, if your message is genuine, interesting and heartfelt - and you're persistent - then it can be done.

Always remember that all media outlets (broadcast, online, print) are desperate for content; hungry machines craving the next news fix. If you have something of value to share, they will want it; it's just about convincing them of its value.

Don't be afraid to say hello, but do expect any media outlet to be busy. Start with the receptionist first and ask initial questions there before you bother the journalists or editor. As a general rule, start small: it's far easier to access free online media sharing outlets (Huffington Post, MindBodyGreen) than it is the national newspapers or television.

Find your feet and hone your skills here. Study what else is being published on these and other sites and find an angle that could work.

There are plenty of online yoga sites too that will be delighted to take your work. Don't expect payment; just see it as a way to grow your brand.

Yoga is a highly visual thing so make sure you capitalise on this. The Two Fit Moms that generated a massive following on Instagram found themselves in demand in the yoga press and the mainstream media because they'd already built a following.

The more you can build your following (in any way) the more appealing you'll be to the press.

Make the news

If you do have something that's truly newsworthy (you've been appointed the president's personal fitness trainer) then shout it to the world. It'll be picked up by anyone and everyone; a story like that would go viral in seconds. Otherwise, make the most of your natural talents: sometimes a photo can work wonders. Doing yoga in an unusual setting, especially if you time it right, can lead to media opportunity.

Dealing with the press

SIMPLE **HACKS** TO NEGOTIATE THE **MEDIA** MAZE

PLAY THE ODDS
Everyone wants to be on the cover of Yoga Journal but there are only a few issues a year. Statistically, it's going to be tough no matter how brilliant you are. Yes, it's possible and it's been achieved by lots of people through the years (check out Paige Held's story how she did it on pages: 240-241), but it's a challenge. Start smaller and work up. Get your face known elsewhere. Any online writing or published image is better than nothing at all.

NO TIMEWASTERS PLEASE
Beware the busy newsroom on deadline. Ask the switchboard what the best day is to approach the journalists. Strike when they're most receptive to new ideas, not when they're sweating it out over the PC late at night.

DON'T TAKE IT PERSONALLY
You're not the only one competing for attention. There are literally thousands of others all vying for the same space. If your story or image is not used, move on. Think it through to make your approach (story or photo idea) compelling to them. They do want your material, but only if it's presented in a way that appeals to them, and if you're straightforward to do business with. Make it easy for them to say 'yes' to you.

BE COURTEOUS
You may not like what you hear back from the newsroom (you may not hear anything) but nothing will kill your relationship with a media outlet more quickly than a few short, sharp remarks. And if there's even a sniff of legal action around, or some other bad feeling, then that organisation may never work with you again.

CHECK YOUR SPELLING
You don't have to be a brilliant writer or published author. All you need to do is to present what you want to say in as few words as possible. Keep it very clear and simple, and save the all fancy stuff for later. However, take time to make sure that your work is presentable and that everything is spelt correctly. The media will smell amateurism a mile off.

BEGINNERS WELCOME
Work on your sales pitch (by email, over the phone, or in person). You just need to convince them that your story is relevant and valuable to them. It doesn't matter if you've never been published before, they won't mind; but don't pretend if you haven't been. A journalist will know if you're telling the truth or not; they might even check up, which, quite frankly would be embarrassing.

have faith

Teaching celebrities

FIRST RULE OF **TEACHING** CELEBS: NEVER TALK ABOUT TEACHING **CELEBS**

There's an interesting phenomenon when it comes to yoga instructors and their celebrity clients. Quite rightly, like any true professional, yoga teachers are reluctant to divulge any personal or private information. So that means no inside gossip on Madonna's private life, or what Gwyneth Paltrow had for lunch that day. Damn!

Annoyingly (but quite ethically correct), it means we are left by ourselves to speculate on such trivial matters, or depend, as always, on trashy gossip magazines for our information. However, whilst all esteemed teachers clearly state that "they don't want to talk about it" when asked about their big clients, they do have a habit of sneaking through a tidbit of information, just enough to let you know that they have rubbed shoulders with the stars.

If you find yourself in this situation, here's some advice to follow from one US yoga instructor who shall remain anonymous:

"Celebrities, when they come to class, don't want to be singled out and we respect their right to their anonymity and treat them like anyone else on the path. It's their private personal time which is invaluable for them. Yoga does attract a lot of musicians and actors, actresses, and singers. It's because it helps to quickly remove mental, emotional, even physical blocks that can keep them from being in the creative flow. It also gives people the strength to let their 'real self' shine through, which is everything to a celebrity. It's usually why people are stars, because they have found a way to be 'themselves' publicly. Celebrities are like everyone else in this way; they are looking for an edge, a way to be just a little bit better all the time. Yoga gives them the means for that."

Just ordinary people

Like it or not, celebrities are highly marketable commodities. Yes, they are people first, and that'll be apparent when you meet and teach them. But simply by association, your media profile will shoot up. Don't chase them, but if they come to you, don't turn them away either.

Ava Taylor (USA)
ARTIST MANAGEMENT / ENTREPRENEUR

YOU DON'T WANT TO POP TOO SOON, SAYS AVA TAYLOR OF CREATIVE YOGA TALENT AGENCY, YAMA TALENT

There's no fast-track to success in the yoga world
Certainly, we have seen the success of savvy use of the internet and social media to create a 'pop' for a yoga teacher, elevating their brand recognition quickly, which I think is a very exciting phenomenon. In order for that rise to be sustained, though, I believe teachers need to provide a superior product - meaning teach some damn good yoga - which usually takes time to develop. If the 'pop' happens to soon, and the product doesn't match the hype, then we're looking at short-term success.

PR can be a huge asset to a yoga teacher | But it's got to be at the right time. Using a media specialist too soon is a common mistake for teachers who are looking to build their name recognition. At YAMA, we generally recommend being sure you have a very clearly presented and packaged brand, as well as employing all free marketing tactics (there are lots of them) and having some type of product or merchandise to sell before launching into any kind of pay-to-play promotional tactics. Getting your 'name out there' only matters when you have the back-end in place to make the most of it.

We get requests from teachers the world over | A lot of yogis come to YAMA to help launch their business and get the word out. We're at the epicentre of the newly emerging yoga industry with an incredible amount of opportunities and relationships that can be leveraged. Joining the agency, and benefiting from our network, acts as a catapult for your brand. Yogis know this and want to be a part of it.

A lot of yogis are accidental business people |
Successful yoga teachers get inundated with business tasks

that often conflict with what they personally need to do to thrive as a teacher. Here at YAMA, we help yogis organise and streamline their existing businesses, build teams, create relationships, so they can do what they do best - teach.

best advice:

1. Build a team: no rockstar yogi is doing it alone.
2. Set clear goals: if you don't know where you are going, you'll end up somewhere else.
3. Be patient: no superstar was born overnight.

have some fun

YOGA ROCKSTAR TIP #20

'KEEP YOUR WORD'

"Build your reputation on
solid ground. Keep your
word and commitments.
Be kind and treat
everyone as an equal."

Cameron Shayne | *USA*

Get Inspired

A YOGA BLOG IS A FANTASTIC WAY TO STAY IN TOUCH WITH YOUR STUDENT COMMUNITY, SAYS STEPHANIE SPENCE

The yoga 'business' has changed so much | When I started practicing, yoga wasn't a 'business' at all. There were no festivals, yoga DVDs, no internet. There were a couple of books floating around, but you had to hunt for them. Now, yoga is a business.

Owning a studio wasn't for me
I got my teaching certificate with the idea that I'd open a studio. I worked at a small place to see what it'd be like to own one: what I saw were long hours and dealing with lots of people for not much money, so I didn't pursue it. Friends of mine that have successful studios also have products they sell or a restaurant attatched, or they lead workshops and retreats.

Reach out to students with a blog
One challenge I face as a teacher is that I love to travel. But every time I go away, I feel awful, like I'm leaving my students to fend for themselves.

I decided the best way for me to stay connected was to start a yoga blog. We all have a voice if we choose to share it.

Build your own brand | Some teachers are reluctant to use the free tools available to them to build awareness about what they have to offer. Use social media to build a unique brand from the start. Take charge and create a website or blog that conveys your teaching style, then use social media to connect with others who could benefit from it.

Don't fret the finances | I have always believed that if I make money I have the capacity to help others more with that money. Do what you love and know the financial questions will be answered for you. Be accountable to yourself. If you operate out of a place of love, you will get what you give and perhaps receive more than you ever dreamed. Share your unique gifts.

best advice:

I believe we are all writers. Cultivate a unique perspective and share what you love. I write from a place of fearless truth; it's the only way I know. If you strive to share your own beautiful unique voice then the words will resonate with others.

Stephanie Spence USA

The business of teaching yoga

THE **RISE** OF THE YOGA 'INDUSTRY' MAY NOT BE A BAD THING FOR THIS **PLANET**

It's easy to argue that business and money have no place in yoga. It's true, yoga can be a rather solitary and even spiritual pursuit for many people (though that's not the case for all). It varies from individual to individual.

For me, it's a place I go to each week to put myself (body and mind) back together after the stresses and strains of the week, and of life, generally.

But there's no point living in denial either. Whatever any of us think, it's fair to say that the world of yoga has got more commercial as it has become more popular.

Lots of yoga pants are now being sold, and it's hard to read a gossip mag without seeing a Hollywood star clutching a rolled up mat under their arm.

Again, it's easy to take the stance that it's all a bad thing. But surely we all want yoga to become more popular, right? Whatever form the yoga might take, I reckon it edges us all closer to a more conscious and ethical planet.

If some people just happen to be making good money out of doing what they love (in this case, yoga), so what? An entrepreneur with a bright idea or a talent should be rewarded (shouldn't they?) whether they work in yoga, soccer or financial services. It's up to them how they attach themselves to that success.

So I don't think we should necessarily equate the rise in popularity of yoga with some inevitable descent into ghastly consumerism. All the teachers I know, without exception, have far too much integrity to follow that path. Yes, we live in a commercial world; we're told to buy things from a young age, that's what makes our economies tick.

But it doesn't have to dilute the message. The person who comes to yoga with a broken body doesn't care about the bright lights, they just want to be healed. Yoga is still there for them, just as it always was.

It certainly hasn't changed my own personal yoga experience. My weekly class is exactly the same: just me and a few pals under the watchful eye of a trained instructor. And that's all I want. I think it's a great thing that yoga is now more popular than ever.

be awesome

Towards conscious capitalism

1 This yoga 'industry' (or whatever you want to call it) is only going to grow. It's super popular now and it's not going to stop anytime soon. I've no idea what the current value of the industry is, or how to go about measuring it, but I believe that if it's worth millions now, it'll be worth many more millions in the years to come.

2 Why? Because the world (the Western world, that is) is stressed out, over-worked and desperate for new ways to stay fit and healthy (not just physically, but mentally too). People, I believe, are discovering that yoga's magical ways can not only keep them trim, but also peel away some of the other pressures of modern life.

3 The simple demographics facing Europe and North America (older populations) means there has to be a new approach to healthcare generally. People will need to take greater responsibility for their own health (what they eat, how they exercise) rather than rely on a medical system that's already buckling under the pressure of too much sickness. That opens doors for yoga, meditation and all other kinds of complementary therapies.

4 Yoga now has a truly global PR opportunity after the United Nations sanctioned June 21 as International Yoga Day. It's an annual showcase for all things yoga. It opens more doors and gets the yoga message out there to more people.

5 Yes, it's also about money these days. The day private equity funds start showing an interest in yoga marks the day when this really becomes an 'industry'. Hey wait! That day is already upon us (Great Hill Partners paid an estimated $45 million for the YogaWorks franchise back in 2014). I'm not saying it's a good or a bad thing. That's just the way it is.

6 Is it possible to get rich from yoga? It's extremely unlikely, but possible. Just ask the YogaWorks guys. Manage your expectations though to avoid disappointment. Let's be honest folks: if money is your primary motivation, don't go into yoga at all, just enjoy a few classes every week without the pressure. Instead, go into private equity funding. You'll get a good pay cheque each month and they'll probably throw in a free gym membership too.

How I made
it happen

EFFORTLESSLY COOL, AND NO STRANGER TO CONTROVERSY, KATHRYN BUDIG SAYS TEACH WHAT MOVES YOU

I'm grateful for my early teachers | Having Maty Ezraty as my teacher was the best break a student could get. I'm grateful for her guidance and loved every single moment. She first connected me with Yoga Journal. I eventually did a photo spread, which lead to a cover, which lead to modeling one of their DVDs, which lead to creating online videos for them. It was a lovely trickle effect that opened doors and gave my teaching credibility.

The naked Toesox ads created a huge stir | Both good and bad. Regardless, it put my name out there and it remained strong even after the dust settled.

You need patience and experience | You need patience to succeed as the yoga world has become quite competitive. You won't be an amazing teacher without time and experience; doesn't matter if you're a prodigy, you need to be out there with your students to truly learn your voice.

Teach what moves you | Yoga needs to stir something deep in your soul. The most successful people I see teach what moves them, not what they think people want to hear. It's so important to dance to the beat of your own drum and find a way to make the information you want to share relatable, accessible and loving.

I feel lucky to have started when I did | We're now in the golden age of social media, where anyone can sell out a workshop if they have enough followers online. This means more competition. My success was slow earned: it took tons of hours, teaching at many studios, lots of travel and plenty of writing. I wouldn't change anything even if I could, but it seems to be more of a popularity contest these days.

Kathryn Budig USA

best advice:

Educate yourself, try as many different teachers as you can. Absorb what you love and leave what you don't. Teach what motivates you. Don't be afraid to unapologetically be yourself in the classroom. That's what will make people love you.

Why I wrote this book

REMEMBER FOLKS: YOU ARE NOT IN THE YOGA BUSINESS, YOU ARE IN THE BUSINESS OF CHANGING LIVES

I desperately want to see people that are selling something remarkable - yoga, health, wellness, life coaching, whatever - to succeed.

Why? Because they have personally brought so much into my own life.

As a journalist, I have spent far too long tracking banks and oil companies who churn out billions of dollars profit each and every month, but leave most of us feeling empty.

Then I started work at OM magazine. It was meant to be: it exposed me to the amazing world of yoga and got me through the toughest time of my life (I won't bore you with the details here).

This book is meant as a sincere, but light-hearted, attempt to share the combined wisdom of lots of fabulous yoga teachers, both new and experienced, with my own time as a writer and editor.

In that time, I've covered all kinds of corporations, large and small, met world leaders along the way (including my hero, former South African president Nelson Mandela) and written copy for esteemed figures such as former British prime minister Tony Blair (don't worry, I didn't make up the Iraq dossier).

It's been a fun journey, although, on the downside, I've also been physically manhandled by burly Algerian security guards, ejected from conferences for asking the wrong questions (no hard feelings, guys), and had a few hair-raising moments in armed convoys in some dodgy parts of the world.

The thing is, what yoga teachers do - what you do - matters so much more than all of that corporate stuff.

This planet desperately needs your services right now. You bring sanity and calm to all this madness.

So I hope you find this book useful (and fun) as you build your own career. Believe anything is possible and it probably is. Time, then, to shine your light on the world.

Go get 'em tiger.

And finally

FOR WHAT IT'S WORTH, HERE' S MY LITTLE SUMMATION OF ALL THE INSIGHT AND ADVICE IN THIS BOOK TO HELP YOU ALONG THE PATH

1 Work on your business, not in it
This is easier said than done when you're charging all over town, leading 20 classes a week, but it's important to take a step back sometimes. Once a week, or once a month, re- visit your goals and visions, otherwise, you'll just get bogged down in all the small stuff.

2 Don't be too quick to judge others
Yoga can be tribal. It's all to easy to view your yoga style above another. We're all on the same side in the end. In my mind, if it calls itself 'yoga', then it's 'yoga'; it's not for me to judge what is or isn't. Just accept this quirky community and all it's funny little ways.

3 Nothing beats hard work
There's no magic formula to success but it's not even possible without hard work (no matter how talented, funny or beautiful you are). Get busy, hustle and get out there.

4 Keep evolving
Keep learning your craft and be open to new ideas. That's how we grow. It'll help you if you ever get stuck in a rut. Don't be afraid to try something new. Your career is not likely to be linear like this book; be excited by all the possibilities.

5 Stay in love with yoga
You want to love this yoga career, not struggle through it like some office job. All these numbers, these challenges, mean nothing if you don't love your business and you don't love your students. Stay in love with yoga: that's your ticket to freedom.

GRATITUDE

A big thanks to all of the incredible yoga teachers, leaders, pioneers, experts, entrepreneurs and business champions that are featured throughout this book. Every single one of you has inspired me personally and in so many different ways (often without you even knowing it). The world is a much better place with you guys in it.

HOW I MADE IT HAPPEN:
Tara Stiles (stralayoga.com)
Eoin Finn (blissology.com)
Katy Appleton (appleyoga.com)
Guru Jagat (gurujagat.com)
Cameron Shayne (budokonuniversity.com)
Faith Hunter (faithhunter.com)
Maya Fiennes (mayaspace.com)
Ana Forrest (forrestyoga.com)
Michele Pernetta (fiercegrace.com)
Kathryn Budig (kathrynbudig.com)

GET INSPIRED:
Bethany Platanella (bethanyplatanella.weebly.com)
Susan Myers (rocketyogastudio.co.uk)
Mandy Carter (yellamella.co.uk)
Paula Hines (ucanyoga.co.uk)
Mercedes Ngoh Sieff (yeotown.com)
Steve Johansen (hummingbirdpilates.co.uk)
Amy Coop (facebook.com/radiantyogi)
Sarah Jane Griffiths (thesarahjanegriffiths.com)
Kathleen Stavert (kathleenstavert.com)
Kate Duncan (kateduncanphotography.com.au)
Carole Moritz (facebook.com/carole.moritz26)
Ann-Margaret Graham (yogawitham.com)
Veronique Gauthier (tamingthewalrus.com/veroniqueyoga.com)
Nikki Ralston (theralstonmethod.com)
Charlotte Watts (charlottewattshealth.com)
Jill Lawson (jilllawsonyoga.com)
Louise Palmer-Masterton (camyoga.co.uk)
Jo De Rosa (innerguidance.co.uk)
Paige Held (theyogajoint.com)
Stephanie Spence (one-with-life.com)

way to go!

INSIGHT:
Photography: **Robert Sturman** (robertsturmanstudio.com)
Goals & Visions: **Lululemon** (lululemon.com)
Marketing: **Alana Littler/Heather Cereghino** (wearecloverpr.com)
PR: Kristin **Ann Janishefski** (thevanguardpr.com)
Franchising: **Cheryl MacDonald** (yogabellies.co.uk)
Retreats: **Peter Simmons** (pjdsimmons@gmail.com)
Video: **Kellie Adkins** (kellieadkins.com)
Studios: **Debbie Lynn** (facebook.com/360degreesofinspiration)
Artist Management: **Ava Taylor** (yamatalent.com)

PHOTO CREDITS:
Phil Munson (p29)
Nir Livni (p21)
Reebok (p32)
Edmund Carter (p43)
Tania Dolvers (p48)
Kate Ediger (p55)
Danylo Bobyk (p64)
Phil Munson (p71)
Eddie Macdonald (p75)
Shadownplay (p88)
Amanda Michaels-Zech (p90)
Drew English (p113)
Philippa Copleston-Warren (p121)
Tracy Mahoney (p141)
Mark Weikert (p151)
Ruud Voerman (p160)
Dean Howard (p203)
Neil Mackenzie Matthews (p233)
Channing Coe (p241)
@hoonphotography (p247)
Robert Sturman (p249)

Big thanks also to Keith Coomber, Julie Saunders and all the team at OM Yoga & Lifestyle Magazine, and to my designer and friend, Graham Williams. This book would not have been possible without you. And finally: massive respect to all of you rock stars cited throughout the book as well (and that goes especially to you, Keith Richards, I know you're reading!). Thanks for the music, guys. We are all made of stars.

dream big dreams